WILLIAM HOARE OF BATH R.A.
1707–1792

WILLIAM HOARE OF BATH R.A.
1707–1792

Victoria Art Gallery Bath
November 3 – December 8 1990

Catalogue by Evelyn Newby

Published by Bath Museums Service and Alan Sutton Publishing 1990

ISBN 0–86299–897–2

Photo credits
The Paul Mellon Centre for Studies in British Art
The Courtauld Institute of Art
Royal National Hospital for Rheumatic Diseases, Bath
Bristol City Art Gallery
National Portrait Gallery, London
National Gallery, London
Los Angeles County Museum of Art (William Randolph Hearst Collection)
The National Trust

Generous financial support for this catalogue has been given by Messrs. C. Hoare and Company and by the Paul Mellon Centre for Studies in British Art.

Cover: Self Portrait by William Hoare (cat 1)
        Royal National Hospital for Rheumatic Diseases, Bath

Typesetting and origination by Alan Sutton Publishing Ltd.,
Phoenix Mill, Far Thrupp, Stroud, Glos.
Printed in Great Britain by The Bath Press, Lower Bristol Road, Bath, Avon.

ACKNOWLEDGEMENTS

I would like to convey my heartfelt thanks to all at The Paul Mellon Centre for Studies in British Art for their help and encouragement during my research for this exhibition, particularly Dr Brian Allen whose advice – often humorous – has been invaluable and Douglas Smith who has provided many excellent photographs often taken in less than ideal circumstances.

Many other people have helped and I have tried to acknowledge them in the catalogue but special thanks must go to the Victoria Art Gallery whose staff have so efficiently taken on all practical difficulties.

My deepest gratitude, however, must go to all the owners, both public and private, who have responded so generously to my requests for loans, even in the case of fragile treasures. Any attempt at an exhibition would have been impossible without their co-operation.

Evelyn Newby
1990

This is the first exhibition to examine the work of William Hoare and it is entirely appropriate that this important event should take place in Bath where Hoare spent the major part of his career. On behalf of the Victoria Art Gallery I would like to thank all those who have assisted with the exhibition, in particular the staff of the Museums and Galleries Commission for arranging indemnity for the exhibition under the Government's National Indemnity Scheme, Alastair Laing, Picture Adviser to the National Trust for all his support for the initial idea and for making several important loans available and Clive Quinnell, Administrator of the Royal National Hospital for Rheumatic Diseases, Bath. Above all I would like to thank Messrs. C. Hoare and Co. and The Paul Mellon Centre for Studies in British Art for their generous financial support for the publication of this catalogue.

Finally my thanks go to Evelyn Newby who selected works for the exhibition, both for her enthusiasm and encouragement and for her excellent catalogue which is the result of considerable research on the artist and which will undoubtedly make an important and lasting contribution to the study of 18th century portraiture.

Victoria Barwell
Arts Officer
Bath Museums Service

WILLIAM HOARE OF BATH R.A.
1707–1792

'An ingenious and amiable English artist'
(Chalmers – 1814)

Introduction

This exhibition is the first to be devoted to the work of William Hoare of Bath and is an attempt to define the oeuvre of an artist who has suffered greatly from neglect and misattribution. In December 1793, a year after his death, when Royal Academicians were deliberating how best to commemorate the 25th anniversary of the Academy's foundation, one of the proposals put forward by the then President, Benjamin West, was for an exhibition 'of dead and living artists, members of the Academy'[1]. The Academicians eventually decided against this scheme, so we do not know by what work or works his fellow members would have chosen to represent him. When in 1951, the Royal Academy organised their winter exhibition *The First Hundred Years of the Royal Academy*, no work by Hoare was included, and if between the years of 1793 and 1951, works by him occasionally appeared in mixed exhibitions, they were mostly the large official portraits of public men, never the more intimate likenesses of friends and family, nor the pastels which are perhaps his greatest contribution to the art of his period. He could only be judged to his own detriment and suffered from a too direct confrontation with Gainsborough and Reynolds.

Many factors have contributed to his neglect, some of a personal, others of a more general nature: a quiet reflective personality, a decided preference for the domestic life, the choice of Bath as a place of residence, an eclectic style which precluded the formation of disciples, and the sudden and complete waning of the popularity of pastel very soon after his death.

Richard Graves, rector of Claverton and friend of Ralph Allen, praised Hoare's character and his learning, describing him as 'not only the most virtuous, friendly and inoffensive of men, but one of the best classical scholars both in Greek and in Latin with whom I was ever acquainted'.[2] In spite of his considerable education, Hoare was never tempted to write works of a theoretical or polemic nature although he took a share in the preliminary discussions on the formation of an academic body, and although surviving letters to Henry Hoare (cat 24) and from Gainsborough[3] show that he was well able to enter into discussions on theory and style. Nor does Hoare seem to have had strong political views. A portrait painter, wishing to establish himself and attract a wide clientèle, would not have been well advised to refuse or discourage sitters on ideological grounds, but even so Hoare seems to have cast his net very wide and indiscriminately from Freemasons and Jacobite sympathisers to the great officers of State in succeeding Administrations. When trying to establish a pattern over the ramifications of patronage, it soon becomes obvious that two factors are uppermost: the connections he made with those Grand Tourists who were in Italy during the years between 1728 and 1737, and those he established during his long years of association with the Royal Mineral Water Hospital.

The choice of Bath as a place of residence at the beginning of his career had been an inspired one. Defoe had written some years before Hoare's arrival that Bath 'was now a resort of the Sound as well as the Sick; and a Place that helps the Indolent and the Gay to commit that worst of Murders, the killing of Time'.[4] Already by the early 1730s, the city with its two 'seasons' offered a continually replenished stream of potential sitters. A correspondent of Jonathan Swift's, Mrs Barber, wrote in 1736 that 'she never saw a painter that came thither fail of getting more business than he could do, let him be ever so indifferent'.[5] At the time of his arrival, Hoare met with no serious opposition, van Diest had painted a series of portraits for Ralph Allen in the late baroque manner and there were no other artists of note. As the city grew, so did the influx of seasonal visitors and Bishop Warburton's *boutade* that Gainsborough, who had arrived in 1759, was running away with all of Hoare's business was an exaggeration. Hoare, then already 52 and at the height of his career, still had to paint some of his best portraits. If anything, the demand for portraiture increased and in 1761 John Oakley was deploring in the London press that 'it is impossible for the craft of man to invent a method to prevent the sale of portraits and looking glasses'.[6] Studio visiting had become an established part of the Bath ritual, and artists set aside special rooms where their latest productions could be viewed by callers without work being interrupted (cat 44).

With the improvement of the post roads, travelling time between London and Bath was progressively reduced. Hoare visited the capital fairly frequently, and his name is connected with many London institutions. A Governor of the Foundling Hospital from 1744, he was one of the signatories in 1755 to an artists' letter to the Society of Dilettanti agitating for the setting up of an official Academy. In 1760, he joined the Society of Arts and from 1761 exhibited at the Society of Artists and in 1769 his name was added to the list of Founder Members of the Royal Academy at the King's special request. However, he was never in London for long enough at a time to follow through these various initiatives and lacking daily contact with the leading artists there, could not play a very sustained role in their deliberations. Residence in London was a prerequisite for nomination to any of the major appointments within the Academy and, on reading through the Minutes of the General Meetings, one realises that Hoare never attended and only ever voted by postal ballot. Although he exhibited fairly regularly, and as late as 1779 when over 70, his position remained peripheral as is reflected by his placing at the edge of Zoffany's *Group Portrait of Academicians* of 1772. Yet he was very much aware of recent stylistic developments, most probably through visiting the exhibitions, for later works often echo, either in painting or drawing, compositions or ideas previously exhibited by other artists.

His painting style was never innovative. At first nearer to the augustan gravitas of Jonathan Richardson than to the polished decorative surface elegance of Thomas Hudson, his brushwork takes on a more feathery subtle aspect no doubt due to the influence of Gainsborough. His use of colour is always distinctive with a preference for saturated colours and soft tonal values corresponding to his lifelong admiration for the Venetian school. Throughout his life, he absorbed and responded to the examples set by the Old Masters, which he was still studying in his later years, and to the latest works by his contemporaries, and next to the direct studies after Giorgione, Titian, Paris Bordone, Reni and Van Dyck, can be recognised echoes of Gainsborough, Reynolds, Nathaniel Dance, Wright of Derby and in the case of very late drawings, even of Hoppner.

His pastel style evolved from the decorative and fresh brightness of the early years to the far more muted and reflective images of his later career. As early as 1738, Vertue was noting 'a particular grace and beauty in the manner of his heads'[7] and it is unfortunate for his reputation that pastel – the medium in which he excelled – should fall out of favour so soon after his death. In 1796, Sir James Wright 'having observed how much crayon painting is fallen off in what he sees at the Exhibitions' donated a pastel by Cotes to the Royal Academy for the instruction of the students.[8] In 1820, Sir Richard Colt Hoare describing the fine set of pastel portraits by William Hoare at Stourhead wrote 'in this room we are gratified with the sight of some very fine specimens of crayon painting, a style now quite unfashionable'.[9]

A seemingly easy medium, though it demanded both sureness and lightness of touch, pastel had been taken up by many unskilled hands among whom the lady amateurs Walpole deplored in a letter to Sir Horace Mann written in 1779 about Lady Lucan's new enthusiasm for oil painting 'for before, she painted in crayons and as ill as any fine lady in England'.[10] With the advent of public exhibitions, pastel needed to acquire a new solidity to enable it to compete on equal terms with painting under difficult exhibition conditions. The more the medium aped the opacity and surface impasto of oil painting, the further it departed from its intrinsic qualities of lightness and grace. By the 1830s, Benjamin Robert Haydon finally damned the medium in a lecture on painting as one of the three poisons of art, together with coach painting and watercolour;[11] in the case of pastel, he was following a general European trend.

1. *The Diary of Joseph Farington*, Yale Edition 1978–84, Vol I, p 107.
2. Rev. Francis Kilvert, *Ralph Allen and Prior Park*, 1857, p 17.
3. Mary Woodall, *The Letters of Thomas Gainsborough*, 1963, pp 95–7.
    The recipient is wrongly identified as Prince II Hoare.
4. Daniel Defoe, *A Tour through Great Britain*, 2nd ed. 1738, p 240.
5. F.E. Ball ed., *Correspondence of Jonathan Swift DD*, 1913, vol V, p 388.
6. *St James Chronicle*, April 27 1761.
7. *The Notebooks of George Vertue*, *Walpole Society*, vol XXII, p 85.
8. *Royal Academy Council Minutes*.
9. Sir Richard Colt Hoare, *The History of Modern Wiltshire*, 1822–1843, vol I, p 73.
10. W.S. Lewis ed., *Horace Walpole's Correspondence*, vol 24, p 475.
11. B.R. Haydon, *Lectures on painting and design*, 1844, vol I, p 324.

Biographical sketch

One of the main difficulties met with in an attempt to chronicle the life of William Hoare in any detail is the lack of a family archive and a dearth of documents.[1] Apart from an autograph letter written to Henry Hoare in 1760 setting down his artistic credo (cat 24), most other extant letters by Hoare are dispersed within the family archives of his sitters and deal with the more mundane matters of framing, carriage, bills and receipts. R. Wright's invaluable notes on Bath artists[2] and the text of a lecture he gave in Bath[3] unfortunately hardly ever give the source of the information he imparts, although it is obvious that Wright had accesss to much which has since been mislaid. It is therefore very tantalising to find in the Beinecke Library at Yale a letter from Prince II Hoare to Thomas Phillips RA, sent from Brighton and partly dated 19 Nov 18 . . ., which promises to furnish Phillips with 'the little notices I have collected respecting my father (which) are among my papers in town. I never saw any edition of Pilkington which contained an account of my Father. Mr Fuseli's had none, and I do not know of any since'.[4] Prince Hoare's papers collected towards a History of British Art are so far untraced.

No birth certificate has ever been found and it would seem that even his children were unsure of the exact date of his birth. The wall tablet in St Swithin's Walcot, Bath, to himself and his wife says he died aged 84 in 1792,[5] but the monument by Chantrey erected in 1828 by his son, Prince II, in Bath Abbey is inscribed: NATUS EST A.D. MDCCVII E STIRPE IN AGRO SUFFOLCIENSI. It is repeated in various early sources that he was educated at a school in Faringdon, Berkshire. In his lecture (op. cit.) R. Wright says that the whole family moved from Suffolk to Berkshire early in Hoare's life. No source is given but a search at the Berkshire Record Office has shown that many Hoares lived in the county, though none can be positively identified.[6]

Lord Chesterfield maintained that 'Greek and Latin and ancient history are ornamental in the opinion of the world and pleasing in one's own closet'[7] and Richard Graves' comments show that the education Hoare received matched up to this ideal.[8] His early proficiency in drawing was recognised at school, and at the yearly prize exhibitions held there, Hoare was said to have 'distinguished himself above his competitors'.[9] His father was prevailed upon to send him to London to study and taking into account the early age at which young men were sent from school to university, we can assume that Hoare reached London in the very early 1720's.

This was an interesting time at which to arrive in the capital. The Hanoverian Succession had weathered the first Jacobite Rebellion and the increasing political stability was all to the benefit of the rising merchant class. In 1719, Jonathan Richardson Snr had published his two Discourses[10] which were meant to educate and encourage the connoisseur by establishing a method for the evaluation of a work of art, thereby introducing a whole new class to the delights of collecting. The social status of the artist had also benefited from the honours bestowed on Kneller (a knighthood, 1715) and Thornhill (a baronetcy, 1720). In 1720 too John Vanderbank and Louis Chéron (the latter recently arrived from study in Italy), had taken over the St Martin's Lane Academy founded by Kneller some time previously. Based in Great Queen Street, it afforded facilities for drawing from the life and probably also from casts after the antique for an annual subscription of two guineas. One of the subscribers in 1720 was Giuseppe Grisoni (Jean-Pierre Grison) a Fleming who had studied in Florence and who had worked as draughtsman for John Talman the architect/antiquarian during the latter's tour in Italy and who was persuaded by him to come to England in 1715. It was with Grisoni that Hoare was apprenticed.[11]

Although there is no proof that Hoare ever attended the Academy his master would most probably have introduced him to most of his fellow members and Hoare may have been encouraged to study from Chéron's collection brought back from Italy. Chéron's sale catalogue[12] includes all the names that Hoare was particularly to admire once in Italy: Raphael, Titian, Tintoretto, Reni, Carracci, Poussin and Brill. Hoare must have been out of his apprenticeship – if such an agreement ever formally existed – by 1728 when 'Mr Grisoni made a sale of his pictures painted by himself designing to leave England, not meeting with encouragement. . . When Mr Grisoni the painter went out of England, he took with him to Italy a young man who had studied drawing some time, had a strong genius, a sober young man'.[13]

Since Grisoni was returning to Italy, he presumably chose the quickest way home, and sailed directly to Livorno avoiding a lengthy journey through France and the difficulties of an Alpine crossing. In Rome, a search in the *Stato delle Anime* registers for the parish of S Andrea delle Fratte[14] has shown that Hoare shared lodgings at 53 via Gregoriana (Palazzo Zuccaro) with Angillis, a painter, and Delvaux and Scheemakers both sculptors, in 1729 and 1730. In 1731 and 1732, only Delvaux still remained with him. This area of Rome, around the Piazza di Spagna and rising by the newly finished Spanish Steps to Sa Trinità dei Monti and the Pincio, was densely populated by foreign artists and tourists, the Caffè degli Inglesi a recognised meeting place for all new arrivals. As Hoare attached himself to the studio of Francesco Imperiali who lived in the Corso, and probably also attended the life classes at the French Academy then situated in Palazzo Mancini in the same street, he probably moved to a new location after Delvaux's departure, a location still untraced.

It was customary in Rome for older students to attach themselves to the studio of an established artist. Francesco Fernandi, called Imperiali, was one such who also counted Batoni and Ramsay among his pupils. He worked in the classicising late baroque style of Maratta and was a popular teacher making a point of taking his students round the sights of Rome. The French Academy had moved to Palazzo Mancini in 1725 and offered well appointed study rooms where students had every facility : daily life classes, a variety of plaster casts, 'character' models and frequent trips to Frascati and Tivoli. When Lord Portland's son visited the Academy in 1727 he wrote home wishing that the same was available for English students. In fact, Vleughels, the Director, was a hospitable man and welcomed students from other nations. The foundation of Hoare's understanding and knowledge of French art certainly dates from his years in Rome. His familiarity with antique sculpture was equally profound. Lodging as he did with two sculptors at the beginning of his stay, it must have been a subject very much to the fore in their discussions, and his appreciation was no doubt enhanced by his thorough classical education, surfacing later in life in many of his compositions. In 1734, well before Hoare's return to England, Clement XII had inaugurated the Capitoline Museum, collecting many of the antique statues scattered about the city together with Cardinal Albani's first sculpture collection in one of Michelangelo's palaces on the Campidoglio.[15] That and the collection housed in the Villa Borghese on the Pincio were favourite places of study for most aspiring artists.

Although Hoare's debt to Rosalba Carriera, the Venetian pastellist, is undeniable, the basis of his technique was more probably acquired in Rome. He had already learnt to draw in red and black chalks but his interest in coloured pastels may have begun with a study of the works of such as Benedetto Luti (1666–1724) only lately dead, whose output had been so large that Lanzi, reacting against the medium in 1795, wrote 'Facesse tanto numero che divennero quasi volgari in Europa. Egli era nato a cose maggiore'.[16] Mariette, the French connoisseur who had done more than most to further Rosalba's career in France recognised that draughtsmanship was not her strong point[17] and appreciated Luti's enough to own a self portrait by him. Hoare's interest in pastel could only have been strengthened by visits to Venice – he had first hand knowledge of the Venetian school which make a stay there a certainty – and it is just possible that he may have met Rosalba herself. He certainly owned two pastels by her in England, but although in feeling and composition, Hoare's early pastels are closest to hers, his technique is Roman rather than Venetian. Rosalba made great use of the stump, blending all the pigments into a delicate sfumato, blurring outlines and depending purely on colour. In less skilfull hands this method can become rather pasty as can be seen in some of Rosalba's other English immitators. Luti's technique, although using stump on the lower layers, consisted in adding individual strokes of pure colour on the surface with a greater attention to modelling.

It was during these Italian years that Hoare formed an enduring friendship with Joseph Spence who was in Rome in 1732 as tutor to Lord Middlesex, later 2nd Duke of Dorset. Spence was to return to Italy a second time, from 1739 to 1741, this time in charge of the young Earl of Lincoln[18] and was certainly the connecting link between Hoare and the Pelham family from whom the former was to receive so many commissions. As Hoare, like many other young artists, supplemented his income by copying old masters for the Grand Tourists, and as Rome was a small city, he certainly met many other young men such as Robert Dingley, Charles Hanbury-Williams,[19] Henry II Hoare, George Lyttelton and Henry Bathurst all of whom were to be his patrons back in England.

When Hoare returned to London in about 1738,[20] the St Martin's Lane Academy was under new management, Chéron had died long before in 1725 and Vanderbank as lately as 1738. The new directors were Isaac Ware, a nominal Palladian who would later work in the rococo idiom for Lord Chesterfield, and William Hogarth who strongly disparaged the Palladian taste of Lord Burlington and his circle. Both these artists were habitués of a number of clubs and coffee houses (the Virtuosi of St Luke, Slaughter's, the Rose and Crown) where artists and professional men – the new collectors – discussed matters of taste. Although Hoare's name never appears in any remaining list of members, he had connections with many of their number such as Arthur Pond, who had preceeded him to Italy and from whom he bought prints, Henry Cheere the sculptor who together with William's brother Prince Hoare had been apprenticed to Scheemakers, and Martin ffolkes, who had his portrait painted by Hogarth as well as Hoare. George Lyttelton, William Pitt and William Warburton (all future sitters) were members of the Prince of Wales's Household, the first named an enthusiastic patron of the new style as was the Prince himself. From 1738, this style was being used in a very public manner in the decoration of the pleasure gardens at Vauxhall. It was a period of ferment and opportunity, yet Hoare does not seem to have been able to establish himself in the capital but departed very soon for Bath.[21]

Some of the possible reasons for Hoare's doing so have already been mentioned in the introduction. It is not known on whose advice he finally decided to remove to Bath, but it is tempting to suggest that John Wood the Elder may have had a hand in it. Wood had been engaged on some speculative building in the capital, all the while planning the development of his native city to which he returned in 1727. By the time Hoare returned from Italy, Wood was in the throes of the first major building programme in which Hoare was to speculate in a small way, buying a 21 ft frontage on the west side of Pierrepoint Street in 1740,[22] a street where both Lord Chesterfield and the Duke of Kingston had houses. Hoare continued Wood's friend and contributed an etching of *Abaris* as frontispiece to the *Essay towards a description of Bath* in 1749. Another influence may have been that of his own brother Prince who set up as a sculptor in Bath after his apprenticeship. Hoare's marriage to Elizabeth Barker, a London merchant's daughter, for which no certificate has been found, must have occured soon after this as their first child Mary was born in 1744. It is to this period that the pastel self-portrait belongs (cat 1). Hanging, as it probably did, in his painting room together with the two Rosalbas he had ordered from Venice, it served as a confident advertisement of what could be achieved in this medium. It is difficult to assess how many pastels were produced during these early years, as so many remain hidden in private collections; both quick and relatively cheap to produce, and serving as a pleasing reminder of a stay in Bath, they were the foundation on which he built up his reputation.

The Earls of Pembroke and Chesterfield were Hoare's first influential patrons. In the late 1730's, Lord Pembroke had commissioned a pastel of his wife and son, and in 1744 may have considered a large family portrait for which only three detailed head drawings are left. Lord Chesterfield who had been very pleased with his bust by Prince Hoare (cat 7), also sat to William (fig 1). It so happens that both Earls were Freemasons, as was Ralph Allen, and although it does not seem that Hoare was one himself, he may have benefited from such a connection. Other early aristocratic patrons were the Dukes of Beaufort. Walpole called the 4th Duke 'a most determined and unwavering Jacobite'[23] and he, his older brother the 3rd Duke, the 3rd and 4th Earls of Litchfield and Sir Watkin Williams Wynn were all drawn by Hoare in the 'true blue frocks and ermine capes'[24] of the Litchfield Hunt, symbol of their political affiliations. Hoare, however, does not seem to have been drawn into Jacobite circles though he would have had ample opportunity to do so in Rome and the Beaufort connection does not seem to have prevented his being accepted within the Allen circle[25] at Prior Park, where his eruditon, quiet dignity and charm of manner soon made him the favourite artist. Ralph Allen and his wife, Pope, Fielding, Richardson and Warburton all sat to him.

All these various strands come together within the pages of the Royal Mineral Water Hospital's Minute Books. The Hospital, built partly through the munificence of Ralph Allen, and among whose early presidents figure both Chesterfield (1744) and Beaufort (1748), opened in 1742. Nash, who had been indefatigable in collecting subscriptions, was also painted by Hoare at the time (cat 10). Hoare himself had been elected a Councillor of the Hospital from its inception, thereby securely establishing his social position in Bath. He took his role very seriously and his name appears almost weekly as one of the Visitors, whose duty it was to oversee the running of the Hospital both in financial and practical matters, and as late as 1788 when in his eightieth year.

The Chesterfield connection probably led to that with Pitt, for both men were in opposition to Walpole[26] and both were regular visitors to Bath on account of their gout. Their portraits, praised for their good likeness, were followed during the 1740s and 1750s by major portraits of other political men: Dupplin, Hardwicke, Newcastle, Pelham, Temple, Walpole. These portraits and their many versions were the basis of Hoare's output in those middle years and certainly supported a busy studio. Farington described Reynolds' studio as resembling 'a manufactory, in which the young men who were sent to him for tuition were chiefly occupied in copying portraits, or assisting in draperies and preparing backgrounds. . . . The consequence was, that his pupils had very little time for deliberate study'.[27] We know the name of a very few of Hoare's assistants. Henry Leake, the son of the Bath bookseller, won a Society of Arts Premium for a drawing after the antique in 1760 but died soon after arriving in the East Indies;[28] John Taylor became a landscape painter. Some of the difficulties inherent in taking on an apprentice are listed in a letter written in 1752 by a certain John Browne to a father hopeful of apprenticing his son: 'Mr Hoare of Bath will take a Boy of generous and good disposition as an Apprentice for seven years for one hundred Guineas, besides the expense of his Board and lodging . . . he says, he shall eat at his Table, but fears he cannot lodge him in his own House . . . I do not believe there is a worthier Man in England; he likewise understands Latin, French and Italian and says he will take Pleasure in speaking these modern Languages with your son as soon as he has been instructed in the Elements of them. . . . I must tell you that he is so very delicate in his Choice that he says that he will not absolutely engage himself, not for a Thousand Guineas, till he has seen the Boy, that he may judge of his Temper as well as Genius'.[29]

It was during those years that Hoare may have entertained the possibility of establishing himself in London, going there in 1752 to paint several portraits for the Pelham family;[30] he probably took part in the very early discussions on the foundation of an official Academy but within a very few months was back in Bath. Although most foreign artists had left London, partly through the worsening of the dynastic and colonial conflicts which led to the Seven Years' War, the older generation (Hogarth, Hudson) were now being challenged by younger men (Ramsay, Reynolds and Cotes). In a list 'of those painters of our nation now living many of whom have distinguished themselves by their performances', 'Pictor' managed to include 54 names, Hoare's among them.[31] Later, Hoare was proposed as member to the Society of Arts by Henry Cheere and paid his subscription from 1760 to 1764.

By the end of the 1750's, Hoare had four children: Mary, William, Anne and Prince, and the pleasure he took in domestic pursuits shows in the very great number of sketches of his wife and children about their daily occupations and at every stage of their development, all instantaneous sketches, never consciously posed. Only a very few were worked up into finished works, although quite a few are contained within a pencilled frame. Hoare mostly uses red chalk, a medium much more popular on the continent, either with loose, rapid lines which suggest rather than define, or with strong hatching creating a chiaroscuro effect, defining shape by light and shade. The great preponderence among these drawings of studies of women and girls standing or sitting and reading books or newspapers illustrates both the easy circumstances in which they lived which allowed them such leisure activities, and also the availability of books and newspapers through the lending libraries which had sprung up in Bath. It was the age of the novel and Fielding, Goldsmith, Richardson and Smollett had all been friends of Allen and presumably of Hoare.

As early as 1749, Vertue had noted that Hoare 'lived in a handsome, genteel manner'[32] and his career reached a high point in the 1760s, both socially and professionally. The deepening friendship with Henry II Hoare was cemented by the marriage of William's daughter Mary to Henry Hoare of Beckenham, a junior partner in the Bank, only a very few years after the marriage of Robert Dingley's daughter to another Hoare cousin. Henry Hoare entertained the young couples, remarking that 'Brides and Bridegrooms arrive here daily and grow up like mushrooms . . . .and I begin to be afraid of opening a door for fear of interrupting their amorous billing'.[33] William had probably first met Henry in Rome, and they later bought prints together at Arthur Pond's[34] and discussed artistic matters (cat 24). William was a frequent visitor at Stourhead, copying old masters,[35] sketching in the park,[36] exchanging gifts (cat 33). Henry Hoare was probably William's most enthusiastic patron, spending the then large sum of £1400 in a very few years, and prepared to spend as much as £200 on a pastel copy of the 'Rubens' in the Pembroke collection.[37] The project which occupied both of them in the mid 1760s was the interior decoration of the Pantheon, where Hoare painted grisaille panels on garden seats which are still extant, and of the Temple of Apollo where the walls were to have been painted with an adaptation of Guido's *Aurora* which they had both admired in Rome.[38] It is to this project that many of the late drawings of dancing figures belong.

To this decade also belongs Hoare's one major foray into large scale historical painting. He had painted a *Christ with the Cross* for a church in Bath (now lost?) but in 1765, he was commissioned to produce an altarpiece for the Octagon Chapel off Milsom Street (cat 32). The building of the Chapel belongs to the second major period of Bath expansion. An elegant design by Lightholer, it was partly subsidised by subscriptions for seats and pews. One of its main selling points was its salubriousness, in contrast to Bath Abbey which was held to be responsible for the prevalence of 'Bath throat' thought to be caused by the exhalations from the burials beneath the flagstones. Hoare could not but be aware of the great altarpiece Hogarth had painted ten years previously for St Mary Redcliffe in Bristol[39] and when in London must have seen those paintings by Hogarth decorating the staircase of St Bartholommew's Hospital, one of which was a representation of the Pool of Bethesda. Although temperamentally far removed from Hogarth's pugnacity and genius for self-advertisement, Hoare was well aware through his connection with the Foundling Hospital of the use Hogarth had made of the charitable institutions to further the cause of British artists in general, and in the following years Hoare was to present works by himself to various Bath institutions (cat 10 and 17), and to one in London (cat 15).

The 1760s also witnessed the beginning of regular public exhibitions in London by members of the Society of Artists. Although Hoare did not contribute to the first one held in 1760, he exhibited the following year (cat 16) and the next (cat 17) and for most ensuing years until joining the Royal Academy, where he exhibited frequently until 1779.

Meanwhile Bath continued to grow, as did the taste for portraiture. With the sharp increase in the number of visitors came a certain lowering of standards. This was already being felt by some of the old *habitués*. Lord

Chesterfield complained in 1766 that 'Here is a great crowd of trifling and unknown people, whom I seldom frequent, in the public rooms',[40] and Walpole wrote that same year to George Montagu that 'to have lived three weeks in a fair appears to me a century'.[41] Some form of portraiture was now available to the smallest purse and adaptable to the most frantic schedule. The Bath Chronicle in 1770 carried an advertisement for miniature portraits taken in hair, 'but a few minutes and one sitting will do', and in 1776 for shadows in profile 'time of sitting no more than a minute and but one sitting required'. In 1792, the year of Hoare's death, one hopeful artist was even offering likenesses 'in the Etruscan and anti-Etruscan manner'. Thomas Beach, who had trained under Reynolds and had worked in and around Bath, made an attempt at organising a Bath Academy, and the first meeting was attended by both Hoare and Lawrence. Its first exibition in 1778 was favourably reviewed in the London press,[42] but the effort seems to have been short-lived, Gainsborough had gone, Lawrence was soon to follow and Hoare, now both elderly and financially secure, drew and painted almost only for his own pleasure and that of a few close friends and associates, distancing himself from the crowd. Throughout these late years, he continued to encourage younger or less fortunate artists. There remains a short correspondence with Alexander Cozens to whose *Principles of Beauty* he subscribed.[43] He befriended the young Ozias Humphry[44] and was so impressed by the talent of the young Lawrence that he wished to send him to Italy at his own expense[45] in the company of his son.

Throughout the 1760s and 1770s, Hoare's portraits had been evolving towards a softer, more natural style. The brushwork becomes more feathery, no doubt a Gainsborough influence, and his sitters no longer pose, but are interrupted at their daily tasks, Anstey from his writing (cat 39), Danvers from his accounting (cat 40). This new informality which had its roots in France in the works of such as Jean Michel van Loo, can be recognised in the works of Nathaniel Dance and also of Joseph Wright of Derby who had tried unsuccessfully to settle in Bath in the mid 1770s.[46] Hoare's pastel style too avoids all decoration, the colour schemes are simplified and muted and his very late drawings with their atmospheric hatchings hardly depend on line to establish form.

When Hoare died, he left all his possessions to his wife, and at her death two years later, the house in Edgar Buildings to which they had moved in 1763 was sold with most of its contents, and although no sale catalogue seems to have survived, the advertisement alone bears testimony to the affluent lifestyle which Hoare had attained.[47] Yet, the wall tablet erected to his and his wife's memory at St Stephen's Walcot would have been very much more to his taste than the grandiloquent monument in Bath Abbey erected in 1828 at a total cost of £522.16.0 by his son Prince II, the general plan for which had been supplied by George Dance, and the sculpture by Francis Chantrey.[48] By 1828, ironically enough, his reputation was already almost totally obscured.

1.   His only grandchild predeceased him, and the descendants of his sister Hannah Russell, the Lewis family, have not been traced since they left Bath in 1905. At the time, they still owned several family portraits, and may have owned documents as well.
2.   R. Wright, *Ms notes on Bath artists*, Victoria Art Gallery, Bath.
3.   R. Wright, *William Hoare of Bath RA* (Ms lecture text), Bath Public Library.
4.   Matthew Pilkington, *Dictionary of Painters*, 1st ed. 1770. Neither this nor subsequent editions in 1798 and 1805 contained any entry on William Hoare. Fuseli's edition of 1810 does however, contrary to Prince's statement, and the entry remained virtually unchanged in the later editions of 1824, 1829 and 1840. The letter is one of the ALS from Prince Hoare to Thomas Phillips, Osborn Collection, Beineche Rare Books and Manuscript Library, Yale University.
5.   The simple inscription reads: *In this vault/ underneath this church/ are interred the remains of/* WILLIAM HOARE Esqr. R.A. / *who died Dec 10th 1792, aged 84/ and of/* ELIZABETH *his wife/ who died Nov 30th 1793/ aged 74.*
6.   Berkshire Record Office, Reading.
7.   Lord Chesterfield, *Letters to Lord Huntingdon*, ed A.F. Steuart, 1923, p 2.
8.   see Introduction, note 2.
9.   A. Chalmers, *A new and general biographical dictionary*, 1814 (enlarged edition), vol XVIII, p 1.
10   Carol Gibson-Wood, Jonathan Richardson and the rationalisation of connoisseurship, *Art History*, 1984 vol VII/1, pp 38–56. The Discourses were entitled *An essay on the whole art of criticism in relation to painting* and *An Argument in behalf of the science of a connoisseur.*
11.   The Notebooks of George Vertue, *Walpole Society*, 1934, vol XXX, p 170.
12.   Francis Russell, Louis Chéron, a sale catalogue, *Burlington Magazine*, 1988, pp 464–7.
13.   The Notebooks of George Vertue, *Walpole Society*, vol XXII, p 85.
14.   The yearly registers of the Stato delle Anime were a parish by parish census of the population, only concerned with the

religion of the inhabitants. Hoare's name appears under various phonetic guises: *Snr Guglielmo Oro Inglese, Snr Guglielmo dell' Oro Inglese, Guglielmo Hor Inglese* and *Guglielmo Or Inglese Eretico.*

15. C. Pietrangeli, The discovery of classical art in eighteenth century Rome, *Apollo*, 1983, pp 180–191.
16. E.P. Bowron, Benedetto Luti's pastels and coloured chalk drawings, *Apollo*, 1980, vol 111, pp 440–7. 'He made so many that they became almost commonplace in Europe. He was born to better things'
17. P.J. Mariette, Abecedario, *Archives de l'art francais* 1851–3, 'Leur belle couleur fait oublier leurs incorrections, car il faut l'avouer, la Rosalba est fort incorrecte; mais il en est d'elle comme du Corrège, ses incorrections visent au grand, et lui sont, ce semble, permises'.
18. Joseph Spence, *Letters from the Grand Tour:* 'A fool at forty is a fool indeed! When I should be getting a good living I am wandering about Italy, and when I should be saying my prayers am thinking of some fine statue . . . Happy, thrice happy, are the plump and rosy country rectors of England, who know nothing of these vanities and spend all their time in drink and devotion!'
19. R.S.B. Peake, *Memoirs of the Coleman Family*, 2 vols 1841, p 20. A letter from Hanbury-Williams to Francis Coleman, British Resident in Florence is dated November 23 1730 and introduces Hoare: 'The gentleman that brings you this is the same I wrote to you about, being him that comes to study there; all favours you do him will be the same as done to myself'.
20. The notebooks of George Vertue, *Walpole Society*, 1934, vol XXII, p 85.
21. *The Gentlemen's Magazine*, vol 8, February 1738, p 98. A rather indifferent poem addressed *To Mr H—e at Bath on painting Miss B's Picture* suggests that Hoare was working in Bath at least as early as February 1738. I am indebted to Dr Terry Friedman for pointing the poem out to me.
22. *William Hoare limner* appears as one of the leaseholders for the west side of Pierrepoint Street, leases for which were given out from 30 May 1740 to 3 Sep 1742.
23. W.S. Lewis ed., *Horace Walpole's Correspondence*, vol 19, p 26. Letter to Horace Mann, 27 March 1745.
24. W.S. Lewis ed., *op. cit*, vol 9, p 289. Letter to George Montagu 19 July 1960.
25. Ralph Allen had been instrumental in warning the Government of plans for the 1715 Rebellion.
26. Lord Chesterfield, *Miscellaneous writings*, 1777, vol I p 88: 'A place of meeting was approved by the antiministerial party . . . Bath was the spot picked for that purpose . . . This elegant town much resembles the Baiae of the luxurious Romans'.
27. J. Farington, *Memoirs of the life of Sir Joshua Reynolds*, 1819, p 69.
28. R. Wright, *Ms notes on Bath Artists*, Victoria Art Gallery, Bath.
29. E. Hughes, *North Country Life in the 18th century*, 1965, pp 92–5.
30. E. Hughes, *op. cit.*: 'He has been sent for on this occasion to draw Mr Pelham's whole family, they preferring him to any painter in London'.
31. 'Pictor', The art of painting and Limning. *Universal Magazine*, 1748, vol III, pp 225–33.
32. The Notebooks of George Vertue, *Walpole Society*, 1934, vol XXII, p 149.
33. Wiltshire County Record Office, Hoare of Stourhead papers T30. Letter from Henry Hoare to Lord Bruce, July 6th 1765.
34. I am indebted to Dr Louisa Lippincott for this information.
35. Wiltshire County Record Office, Hoare of Stourhead papers T 36. Letter from Henry Hoare to Lord Bruce, 13 December 1765: 'Mr Hoare will on Monday evening enrich Bath with three of the finest heads he ever did from my Judgement of Hercules [by Poussin]'. These were admired by Dorothy Richardson in 1770: 'The Choice of Hercules . . . the Three Heads are put in one Gilt Frame; but divided by a very narrow Gold Moulding as I imagine a Glass cou'd not be got large enough for the whole' (see cat 44).
36. William Hoare exhibited A *view in the gardens of Henry Hoare Esq., at Stourhead, Wilts* at the Royal Academy in 1770. In 1778, Hoare may have painted another view, for in a letter to Lord Bruce dated 6 September (Wiltshire County Record Office, Hoare of Stourhead papers), Henry Hoare wrote: 'Mr Hoare's picture from the Umbrella [a garden feature no longer extant] is here. I think it in the style of Paul Brill or Brilliant and has great merit & a masterly mannr. [sic] – and uncommon'.
37. Henry Hoare's Private Account Book 1739–70, Hoare's Bank Archives. '1762 Mr Hoare of Bath for 4 boys after Rubens £200.0.0.'
38. J.D. Hunt & P. Willis, *The Genius of the Place: the English landscape garden 1620–1820*, 1975, pp 272–3. In 1765, Joseph Spence wrote to the 1st Duke of Newcastle a description of the gardens he had just visited: 'the very back of ye Seats (in the Pantheon) are painted with other relievo's in chiaroscuro by Mr Hoar. Guido's Aurora, enlarged by the Seasons following the Chariot of Apollo, & Night flying before her, is to be painted round the inside of the walls (of the Temple of Apollo) by Mr Hoar'
39. The altarpiece, a large irregular triptych, now hangs in the Bristol City Art Gallery. A central panel of the *Ascension* is flanked by scenes of the *Sealing of the Tomb* and the *Three Maries at the Tomb.*
40. Lord Chesterfield, *Letters to his son*. This letter is dated December 9th 1766.
41. W.S. Lewis ed., *op.cit.* vol 10, p 231, Walpole to Montagu, Bath 18 October 1766.
42. *Bath Chronicle* 16 April 1778. 'Exhibition of the Polite Arts in London: the Artists are encouraged to join their efforts to form one in Bath and intend to open it the 23rd instant at Mr Beach's, Westgate Buildings. No copies will be admitted' The

same paper reported on April 30th that 'A London Artist who had seen the Bath Exhibition of paintings remarks that (as it is only in its infancy) it reflects no small honour on the genius of the Bath artists in general'.

43. *Principles of Beauty relative to the Human Head* 1778. A folio copy in the British Museum lists William Hoare among the subscribers. I am indebted to Dr Kim Sloan for this information.

44. Royal Academy Library. Life of Ozias Humphry: 'Mr Gainsborough's pictures were always within easy reach as well as Mr Hoare's, from both of which he derived considerable light and instruction'.

45. Fanny Burney wrote in her Diary on April 7 1780, 'Mr Hoare has been so charmed with this sweet boy's drawings that he intends sending him to Italy with his own son.'

46. A.C. Bemrose, *The Reliquary*, vol IV April 1864, pp 209–18: 'I have now passed one season, the biggest of the two, without any advantage . . . I am confident I have some enemies in this place . . .'. Hoare was actually well disposed towards Wright, casting his postal vote in Wright's favour at Academy elections.

47. The *Bath Chronicle* for 9 January 1794 gives advance notice of a sale to be conducted on the premises by Mr Plura. Apart from Lot 1 (The lease of the house in Edgar Buildings with a long garden and detached building at the end), Lot 2 (One share in the New Assembly Rooms) and Lot 3 (A pew in the Octagon), the contents included 'a fine-tuned pianoforte, an organ by Gauer, and a capital harpsichord with double keys by Tschudi). On the 18th February, the remainder of his studio was to be sold and on the 19th, other household goods.

48. *Chantrey's Ledger*, p 176. Royal Academy, Library and Archive. 'July 16 1828 to executing a monument according to approved design £500.0.0'

The Hoare Family

William Hoare's younger brother Prince, born in 1711, had studied under Scheemakers together with Henry Cheere. He settled in Bath where his sister Hannah kept house for him until her marriage.[1] 'A tall, handsome and agreeable person somewhat skilled in music',[2] he seems to have been a social success, happy to oblige such as Lady Luxborough with elegant designs for papier mâché ceiling decorations.[3] He had already undertaken some important commissions (cat 7) but was persuaded to travel to Italy where he perfected the sound technique taught him by Scheemakers and became known for his excellent copies after the antique.[4] Soon after his return to Bath, he married well, a Miss Coulthurst with £6,000. His dilatoriness with commissions often embarassed his brother and his output did not live up to his early promise. He died in 1769 leaving the contents of his studio to his nephew Prince II.

William and Elizabeth Hoare had four, or perhaps five, children: Mary (1744–1820) an amateur artist who married into the banking family, Anne (1751–1821) who died unmarried, Peter Paul William, known as William (1752–1809) who became a merchant banker and Prince (1755–1834) an artist and writer. R. Wright also mentions a Georgiana who was baptised in October 1759;[5] there is no further trace of her and she may have died in infancy.

Mary Hoare was born at a period when women who were considered ladies were not encouraged to become professional artists, though her father thought enough of her abilities to take her in hand himself quite seriously. In the letter to Henry Hoare written in 1760 (cat 24), he details her course of study: 'It is my endeavour and desire to make the subjects she is employed in a lesson to herself as well as an exercise of her ingenuity'. Most of her training was at home, copying either from books of engravings or her father's own drawings. She drew well enough in 1760 to win the gold palette for a drawing by a young person under sixteen at the Society of Arts. Although her name was mentioned in the press,[6] she was neither allowed to collect her prize nor to write a note of acceptance, Robert Dingley performing both tasks on her behalf. She exhibited at the Society of Artists in 1765 just before her marriage, and once again the following year. From then on she could only draw as an amateur, mostly portraits of her family and immediate circle of friends. Although her married home was in Beckenham, Kent, where she became the close friend of the three daughters of Sir Peter Burrell, because of her husband's position in Hoare's Bank, she spent a lot of time in London, residing in the Adelphi where she was a near neighbour and particular friend of the Garricks.[7] She and her husband were also close friends of the 10th Earl of Pembroke, the two men collaborating in the breeding of bulldogs.[8]

Her younger sister Anne is an altogether more shadowy figure. She seems to have had no artistic skills but may have been the archivist of the family, pasting books of cuttings and perhaps responsible for the gathering of her father's drawings into albums. After Mary's widowhood, the two sisters seem to have lived together and share a monument in the Chislehurst churchyard.

In 1768, William Hoare was buying an apprenticeship for his son William in a merchant bank and calling in his bills.[9] Later in life, Prince II was to say of his brother that he was as rich as a Jew, and when William Jnr died in 1809 he was able to bequeath £25,000 to his younger brother and £5,000 to each of his sisters.[10] He seems to have inherited some of the family's musical and artistic skills: 'The Prince [his brother] and I have been studying music, though mine has rather stood still of late, but I do not think either of us are fit to play in public yet. It is too troublesome. I believe I shall leave it off and begin painting which you [James Northcote] say I may do to a degree'.[11]

Prince Hoare, born in 1755, was educated at King Edward's School in Bath. In 1773, he was accepted as a painting student by the Royal Academy Schools which suggests that he had already attained a certain proficiency in drawing, having been taught by his father. He left for Italy in 1776 with a generous allowance and many letters of introduction, and in Rome formed part of an avant-garde circle of young artists which included Fuseli. Soon after his return in 1780, he began exhibiting large historical paintings at the Royal Academy but in a few years 'delicacy of health' sent him to Portugal and 'he relinquished that pursuit [art] and devoted himself to Literature'.[12] More honestly, Prince told Farington that 'he had quitted his profession because he found that he could not succeed in the practice as he wished'.[14] At first, he wrote plays and musical comedies but increasingly turned his mind and energies to art theory and the encouragement of an English School. In 1799 he became Secretary for Foreign Correspondence at the Royal Academy, a few years after the death of James Boswell, the first incumbent. He died in 1834 as the result of a carriage accident.

1. R. Wright, *Ms lecture notes*, Bath Public Library.
2. The Notebooks of George Vertue, *Walpole Society*, 1934, vol XXII, p 152.
3. Marjorie Williams, *Lady Luxborough goes to Bath*, 1946.
4. W. S. Lewis ed., *Walpole Correspondence*, vol 20, p 86. Letter from Horace Mann to Walpole 26 August 1749: 'He is very

Plate 1 Cat. no. 1
Self Portrait
Royal National Hospital for Rheumatic Diseases, Bath

Plate 2   Cat. no. 3
Gentleman from the Camden family
The Executors of Fifth Marquess Camden

Plate 3 Cat. no. 4
Lady from the Camden family
The Executors of Fifth Marquess Camden

Plate 4 Cat. no. 16
John Pitt of Encombe, Dorset, His Wife and Son
Private Collection

Plate 5   Cat. no. 19
The Three Sons of the 9th Earl of Lincoln
The Trustees of the late 7th Duke of Newcastle

Plate 6 Cat. no. 22
Henry Hoare the Magnificent
Trustees of the Savernake Estate

Plate 7 Cat. no. 23
Susannah Hoare, Lady Dungarvan
Trustees of the Savernake Estate

Plate 8 Cat. no. 38
Masters Thomas and John Quicke
Private Collection

clever in copying but I have seen nothing original of his doing. Had he application equal to his skill, I believe he could make a figure at least in England, where sculpture is not at any great pitch'.

5. R. Wright, *Ms lecture notes, Bath Public Library*.
6. *Bath Advertiser*, May 10 1760: We hear that the gentlemen of the Society for the encouragement of Arts, Manufactures & Commerce in London judged the first prize of a gold medal for the best drawing by young ladies under sixteen years to Miss Hoare of this city. This repeats a notice which had appeared in the *London Chronicle* a few days previously (No 525, 6–8 May).
7. In a letter of 1778, which among other topics invites Mary Hoare to hear a performance of Judas Maccabeus from Garrick's private box at Drury Lane, he addresses her as 'Sweetest of Canaries'.
8. Lord Herbert ed., *Henry, Elizabeth & George 1734–1780. Letters and Diaries of Henry, Tenth Earl of Pembroke and his circle*, 1939. In a letter of March 1785, Lord Pembroke wrote in a postcript from Naples on hearing of the death of Mary's husband: 'H Hoare had a bitch of mine, I think he called her Tisiphone, but am not certain. She is, I dare say, at Beckenham, & probably Mrs H cares not about her. I should not be sorry to have her again . . . . . . & if ye get the bitch, have her lined immediately, as I have lost my breed'
9. Wiltshire County Record Office, Hoare of Stourhead papers. Letter from Henry Hoare of Beckenham to Lady Ailesbury. 'I am desired by Mr Hoare to present his best Compts to your Ladyship & to acquaint you, that as he is now collecting his Bills in order to pay for his son's prentice fee, he begs the favour of your Ladyship to remit me his little bill'. The bill was for £63.00 for four fancy pictures.
10. Public Record Office, PROB B11/1475.
11. Anderdon (grangerised edition), Royal Academy Library, under William Hoare RA.
12. Webb, Miller & Beckwith, *The History of Chislehurst*, 1899, p 417. This volume records the inscriptions to Prince, Mary and Anne Hoare who are all buried in the churchyard of St Nicholas.

WILLIAM HOARE CATALOGUE

1 Self Portrait (Plate 1)

Medium: Pastel, 19 ½ × 15 in 49.5 × 38.1 cm
Prov: Prince II Hoare, bequeathed to the
    Mineral Water Hospital, 1834
Coll: The Royal National Hospital for
    Rheumatic Diseases, Bath

An entry in the Hospital Minutes, dated 13th December 1780, thanking William Hoare for his gift of the portrait of Charles Danvers (see cat 40), noted 'that he be requested to make the Hospital a present of his own'. A deputation was sent to convey both the thanks and the request but the portrait only reached the Hospital after his son's death. The frame, of the type commonly used by Hoare for his early pastels, bears the date 1742. By then Hoare was securely settled in Bath, had bought a house in one of John Wood's first developments and was probably already or about to be married to Elizabeth Barker, the daughter of a London merchant. He had also become an *habitué* of the Ralph Allen circle and one of the first Councillors to the newly opened Royal Mineral Water Hospital. The portrait, which exists in two (and possibly three) autograph versions,[1] is both an affirmation of his status and an advertisement of his considerable skills as a pastellist. Hoare portrays himself with the same youthful self confidence and elegantly casual *deshabillé*, as does Ramsay in his self portrait soon after his own return from Rome. Both Hoare and Ramsay choose to present themselves as leisured, and by implication, cultured men and neither have recourse to any pictorial allusion to their calling.

1. Another version was bequeathed by Prince Hoare to the Royal Academy and a third was in the possession of the Lewis Family in 1905.

2 Mary Bright (1715–1753)

Medium: Pastel 25 × 18 in 63.5 × 45.7 cm
Prov: By family descent
Coll: Private Collection

Mary Bright married as his second wife Edmund Tyrrell of Gipping Hall, Suffolk, in 1743/4, and the pastel was almost certainly made on the occasion of her betrothal or marriage. An inscription, in Hoare's hand, on the back of the lining canvas reads: *For Mrs Bright at/ Packingham near Bury/ St Edmonds (sic)*

Cat 2

Suffolk/ by the Bury carrier/ you must pack it in a/ case and send it forthwith. Hoare's early pastels were very consciously based on Rosalba types. Soon after settling in Bath, he was said to have sent for two pastels by her – an *Apollo* and a *Spring* (both of which feature in Prince II's will). Rosalba's style was well known in England, as many of the young Grand Tourists sat to her when passing through Venice on their way north and home. Hoare quickly realised that pastel was just as suited to Bath and its seasonal visitors as it was to Venice and the throngs who came to the Carnival. Its speed of execution and comparative cheapness made it an irresistible novelty, a couple of sittings attended by one's friends creating a pleasant diversion during the day. The freshness of tone and the decorative glitter of glass and gilt explain Hoare's rapid rise in popularity.

2a Album of Drawings

Medium:	An album of dark blue-grey leaves containing 104 drawings mostly in black and white chalks on grey or blue-grey paper
Prov:	Sir Thomas Phillips
Coll:	The Trustees of the British Museum

This is one of the considerable number of his Father's albums mentioned by Prince Hoare in his will and distributed among his friends after his death. It is also one of the few to have remained intact. It seems that the drawings were pasted in a vaguely thematic way and this album mostly contains ideas, in black and white chalks, for head and shoulder portraits of women. Many of them look as though they may have been initial proposals for pastels, as they are on the whole too indefinite to be records of finished works. The album is opened at a page with several such sketches, one of which is close to the type of cat 2.

Cat 2a

3 Gentleman from the Camden Family (Plate 2)
4 Lady from the Camden Family (Plate 3)

Medium:	Pastel 25 × 18 in 63.5 × 45.7 cm
Prov:	By family descent
Coll:	The Executors of Fifth Marquess Camden

Both pastels date from the mid 1740s, and although the identity of the sitters has been lost, they may represent John Pratt of Wildernesse and Bayham (1719–1797) and Sarah Eyles whom he married in

1747. Although he is dressed conventionally, she is shown wearing a masquerade adaptation of the dress of a shepherdess. The style is still close to Rosalba and great attention and dexterity is lavished on surface details such as the wig and brocade waistcoat in the male portrait. In the female portrait, the lace trimming of the chemise is delicately handled allowing the black underdrawing to show through, adding to an impression of softness and airiness.

5 **John Jesser** (?–1756)
6 **Elizabeth Jesser** (?–1753)

Medium: Oil on canvas 30⅜ × 25⅜ in   77.2 x 64.5 cm
            30½ × 25⅜ in   77.5 x 64.5 cm
Prov: 1767 Mary Jesser's bequest to her brother John (1); by family descent to F.B. Leach, presented 1947 to Bristol Museum & City Art Gallery
Exh: Exeter, *Treasures from the West Country,* 1937 (cat 87 as Mr Richard Jesser)
Coll: City of Bristol Museum and Art Gallery

Cat 5

When Defoe had passed through Frome on one of his tours earlier in the century, he had described the town as larger than either Bath or York, and a manufacturing town of some wealth. John Jesser was one of the several successful clothiers established there; his family was friendly with Lord Cork, one of whose seats was close by at Marston, and whose unexplained nickname for Jesser appears in a letter he wrote to Lady Cork on the occasion of Mrs Jesser's death: 'Marston March 26 1753 . . . the wife of Pontius Pilate Jesser and mother of Dick Jesser died today suddenly, but Pontius Pilate will hold out to the Day of Judgement'.[2] The portraits probably date from the late 1740's, and Hoare presents both sitters in a very straightforward way with no pretensions to elegance or fashion, as two strong characters secure in their position and conscious of their worth. The faces are strongly modelled and show the same uncompromising yet dignified rendering of age that one finds in the work of George Beare then active in and around Salisbury.

1. 'My Father and Mother and two Brothers' pictures done by Hoare', M McGarvie, *Argyll House, Frome. A Family and Architectural History* 1979, p 22.
2. Lady Cork & Orrery, *The Orrery papers*, 1903 p 201.

Cat 6

7 Philip Dormer Stanhope, 4th Earl of Chesterfield (1694–1773) by Prince I Hoare

Medium: Marble, 28 in 71 cm high (including the socle)
Prov: John Horan, Castlegar, Co Galway
Coll: Joanna Barnes Fine Arts

Frequently throughout his brother Prince's life, William worked closely with him, carrying out commissions for the same patrons. It is therefore interesting to compare the sculpture with the pastel (fig 1), which it complements and with which it (or perhaps the original plaster) is possibly contemporary, dating from before Prince's trip to Italy (1742–47). Here is Chesterfield 'al antica', contemporary trappings (except for the totally incongruous though half hidden Garter Star) abandoned in favour of cropped hair and toga. However, the bust, inscribed PH in monogram at the back, delineates the same thick eyebrows and heavy-lidded eyes, the cleft chin and lined cheeks of the pastel.[1] Several versions of this bust seem to have existed[2] as at that time it was customary to make marble versions of a terracotta or plaster original taken from the life. The Irish provenance of the bust is explained by the fact that Chesterfield was Lord Lieutenant of Ireland from 1765 to 1766, a period during which he had tried to promote Irish industry.

1. Bonamy Dobrée, *Letters of Philip Dormer Stanhope, 4th Earl of Chesterfield*, 1932, p. . . 'It [the bust] is generally thought very like'
2. Francis Russell, Canaletto and Joli at Chesterfield House, *Burlington Magazine*, vol 130, 1988, pp 627–30: the 1815 inventory of Chesterfield House mentions 'a plaister bust of the Great Earl of Chesterfield' (the original?), and Chesterfield himself mentions another bust in the possession of a Mr Adderley in 1752 (Dobrée, *op. cit.*)

Cat 7

Fig 1

8 **Sir Matthew Fetherstonhaugh** (1714–74)
9 **Sarah Lethieuiller, Lady Fetherstonhaugh**

Medium: Pastel 23¼ × 17¼ in 59 × 43.8 cm
Prov: Painted for the sitters; by family descent
Coll: The National Trust, Uppark

Sir Matthew's Grand Tour from 1749 to 1751 was an unusual one in that he made it in the company of his wife, whom he had married in 1746, and after he had inherited a fortune from a distant kinsman. The dating is undocumented, but the pastels were probably drawn early in their marriage and before their departure to Italy.[1] Not only are they in the earlier type of frame used by Hoare for his pastels until about 1750, but it is unlikely that the Fetherstonhaughs would have commissioned such portraits after having taken delivery of the dashing likenesses made for them in Rome by Batoni in 1751. It may indeed have been Hoare who gave them a special introduction to Batoni, whose fellow pupil he had been in Rome and whose friend he had remained, an introduction which enabled Sir Matthew to commission several works from an artist who was known for keeping his patrons waiting many months for their portraits. These two pastels belong to a transitional period; although Lady Fetherstonhaugh is almost certainly in masquerade costume as a Savoyarde,[2] both portraits show a new attempt at a more imposing style.

1. The only portraits known to have been commissioned by Sir Matthew before the Italian trip were a series of small full-lengths by Arthur Devis, which may well have seemed very unsophisticated after their return.
2. During the winter months, many peasants from Savoy worked as street musicians in major European cities, and adaptations of their regional costume was often used as masquerade dress.

Cat 8

Cat 9

10   Richard Nash (? –1761)

Medium: Oil on canvas 29⅜ × 24 in   74.5 × 61.1 cm

Prov: In 1762, the year after Nash's death, the Minutes of the Corporation record on February 20th that 'the offer of Mr William Hoare of a present of Mr Nash's picture to be set up in the Town Hall, to be accepted with thanks'.

Coll: Victoria Art Gallery, Bath City Council

Cat 10

Connelly states in his biography[1] that Hoare painted Nash in 1749, this was over forty years after Nash had begun regulating Bath society and turning the small watering place into a centre of fashionable life. Nash is said to have sat to Hoare at the home of Wiltshire a common friend.[2] They could not fail to have known each other especially through their common involvement in the affairs of the Hospital towards the foundation of which Nash had been working indefatigably long before Hoare ever came to Bath. It is also said that Nash commissioned from Hoare a set of 'Beauties of the age' to be drawn in crayons for the decoration of his house in St John's Court.[3] These were dispersed at the time of Nash's final sale and can no longer be traced, but probably belong to Hoare's earliest years in Bath. Nash, whom Goldsmith had described as a man 'who had too much merit not to become remarkable yet too much folly to arrive at greatness',[4] is shown in late middle age. The signs of over-rich living have not been glossed over, and his considerable bulk quite fills the available space. He is shown wearing the distinctive and by then sligthly old-fashioned clothes he affected as a kind of uniform, the white beaver over a full black wig, the brown coat over a brocaded waistcoat.

1. W. Connelly, *Beau Nash, Monarch of Bath and Tunbridge Wells*, 1955, p 146.
2. Wiltshire ran, among other ventures, a fleet of carriers (Wiltshire's Flying Waggons) which Gainsborough and Hoare both used to convey their works to London.
3. Philip Thicknesse, *The New Prose Bath Guide* 1778, p 81: 'Within, indeed, it was furnished with the beauties of the age, painted in crayons, chiefly by the ingenious Mr Hoare'.
4. O. Goldsmith, *The Life of Richard Nash of Bath Esq*, 1763, p 4.

11 **Richard Laurence** (1729–1773)
12 **Elizabeth French, Mrs Laurence** 1728–1808)

Medium: Pastel 23¼ × 17½ in 59 × 44.5 cm
Prov: Painted for the sitters; by family descent
Coll: Private Collection

Richard Laurence, originally of Warminster, had been apprenticed in Bath from 1744 to 1751. In 1754, he married the daughter of a Warminster clothier and settled in Bath as a watch and clock maker. Their son, Dr French Laurence, became the friend and literary executor of Edmund Burke. The two pastels probably date from 1754, the year of the sitters' marriage and their lighter more sophisticated frames are typical of those used by Hoare during the 1750s and 1760s. A comparison with catalogue 3 and 4 will show that these pastels are altogether more serious in intent, both in style and presentation. It would seem that Hoare planned a trip to Paris and the Netherlands in 1749–50. All we know is that it was cut short by the death of his sister Hannah Russell, but he must at least have reached Paris, and in picking up the strands of friendships laid down in Rome become aware of the works of those pastellists, so successful at the yearly Salons of the Académie, who had adapted their style to withstand competition with oil paintings. The Venetian decorative playfulness has gone, and great care is taken to give the figures solidity by the careful lighting of the background and the choice of a more sober palette.

Cat 11

Cat 12

13 **William Pitt,** later 1st Earl of Chatham (1708–1778)

Medium: Oil on canvas 50 × 40 in 127 × 101.5 cm
Prov: Lord Rosebery sale, Christie's 5 May 1939 (58); Spinks 1947
Coll: Private collection

Cat 13

The existence of at least two fully autograph versions of this portrait is implied in correspondence between Pitt and Lord Temple, his friend and political ally of long standing, soon to become his brother-in-law: 'My picture will before now have come to your Lordship's hands, or rather I shall have had the honour to present myself before you in my very person; not only from the great likeness of the portrait, but, moreover, that I have no right to pretend to any other existence than that of a man en peinture'.[1] Pitt was in Bath at the time suffering acutely from gout. Two months later, he wrote again, probably about a second version: 'I have reconsidered Mr Hoare's labours of yesterday, and I find it the very best thing he has yet done, in point of likeness'.[2] The version, exhibited here, which once belonged to Lord Rosebery, Pitt's biographer, is of high quality, the face, hands and lace strongly painted. By 1754, Pitt had already been some twenty years in politics yet had only reached the position of Paymaster General to the Forces, George II's intense dislike of him hindering further preferment.

1. G. Grenville, *The Grenville Papers*, 1852, pp 120–1 : letter dated March 24 1754
2. G. Grenville, *op. cit.*, pp 120–1 : letter dated May 3 1754

13a **William Pitt**

Medium: Black and white chalks 15½ × 11 in 40 × 28 cm
Coll: The Estate of the late Sir Edward Hoare, Baronet

A careful drawing of the sitter's face, this may have existed as a studio reference for subsequent versions of

the large oil, for this portrait is one of the most
frequently repeated images in Hoare's oeuvre. Seven
versions of the large ¾ portrait have so far come to
light, and many half lengths all using the same
pattern. The number of versions of this and others of
Hoare's main political portraits from the 1740s and
1750s are the main proof of the existence of a busy
studio, but we know nothing of its working methods
and very little of the quality of the assistants
employed, nor even whether all the copies were done
under Hoare's direct supervision, but as the quality of
some of the versions (particularly ½ lengths) descends
so far below a certain standard it is difficult to believe
that they were the official products of such a studio.
The interesting point about all these versions is that
although they must have been produced over a
considerable period of time, they allow for no sign of
ageing in the sitter.

Cat 13a

13b   William Pitt and Henry Bilson Legge

Medium: Mezzotint by Johson, inscribed: *William
          PITT Esq. Henry Bilson Legge esq/ Utrum
          horum mavis accipe*
Lit: Chaloner Smith, *British Mezzotinto
          Portraits*, 1883, vol II p 739, (CS52)
Coll: The National Portrait Gallery

Henry Legge had been Chancellor of the Exchequer
from 1754 to 1755. Ignored by Newcastle, he sought
an alliance with Pitt and after the change of
administration in 1756 was recalled by him. This
mezzotint cobbled together by Johson from two
separate plates, with the figure of Pitt in reverse, was
a record of this political event and was still available
in 1765 – long after the partnership had broken up –
when the Rev James Woodforde noted the purchase
for three shillings of three framed prints of 'Their
Majesties, Mr Pitt & Mr Legge, Prince Ferdinand &
the Marquess of Granby'.[1]

1.   J. Beresford ed., *The diary of a country parson, the Rev
     James Woodforde 1758–81*, 1949, p 34

Cat 13b

13c William Pitt

Medium: Mezzotint by J Spilsbury dated 1761 and inscribed: *The Right Honourable William Pitt Esqr/ one of His Majesty's Principal Secretaries of State/ and one of His Majesty's most Honble Privy Council.*

Coll: The National Portrait Gallery

Finally summoned by the King in 1756 to form a Ministry, Pitt himself took the office of Secretary of State for the South and was responsible for the reorganisation of the war effort, as the war had been dragging on unsuccessfully. The victories that followed on land and sea made him a popular figure and the leading engravers of the day had to meet a large demand for prints. Increasingly weak adaptations of these were further used as book illustrations, for political broadsheets and satirical prints, and the image was even transferred onto china mugs and plaques.

Cat 13c

13d William Pitt

Medium: Mezzotint by Richard Houston inscribed: *The Right Honourable William Pitt Esqr/ One of His Majesty's Most Honble Privy Council.*
21⅝ × 16¾ in   55 × 42.5 cm

Lit: Chaloner Smith, *op.cit.*, vol II, p 680 (CS94)

Coll: The National Portrait Gallery

Immediately under the image is the line *Done from an original Picture in the Possession of Earl Temple by Richd Houston.* There is no known painted version of Pitt wearing a flower-patterned coat, though similar printed velvet coats were fashionable at the time. The pattern may be an invention of the engraver's, for the sprays of flowers seem to be superimposed onto the folds in a rather arbitrary way and may have been a device used to break up what would otherwise have been a rather dull area on so large a scale. Pitt had been a Privy Councillor since 1746, and this large image seems to have been printed in 1766, immediately prior to his elevation to the peerage as Earl of Chatham.

Cat 13d

13e The Distressed Statesman

Medium: Etching by the Marquess Townshend
Coll: The Trustees of the British Museum

A witty adaptation of Hoare's three quarter length, here increased to full length, the etching is given a fanciful attribution to Leonardo da Vinci[1] and shows how familiar the image was within the world of politics. Etched in April 1757 by Lord Townshend who ranked politically as an 'independent', and advertised in the *Gentleman's Magazine* in June,[2] it replaces Hoare's confident image of the hopeful politician by that of the disgruntled statesman after Pitt's (short-lived) resignation from the Ministry. The inscription *1761 vide 1757* may have been added to the plate in 1761 when Lord Townshend brought it up to date after Pitt finally resigned when the Peace party prevailed.

1. The attribution to Leonardo is particularly, but probably unwittingly, amusing as we know Hoare's own strictures on Leonardo's style (cf cat 24).
2. Stephens & Hawkins, *Catalogue of Prints and Drawings in the British Museum: Political and Personal Satires*, 1877, vol III, Satire 3594.

Cat 13e

14 Ralph Allen (1693–1764)

Medium: Oil on canvas 50 × 40 in   127 × 101.5 cm
Prov: Commissioned in 1758 for the Royal Devon & Exeter Hospital
Coll: Exeter Health Authority

The Hospital at Exeter had been founded by Dean Alured Clarke in 1741 and Ralph Allen had long been one of its benefactors when he was elected Treasurer in 1758.[1] That summer, Bishop Warburton, Allen's nephew-in-law, staying *en famille* at Weymouth, mentioned in a letter to Richard Hurd that his small son was 'much taken with Mr Hoare's pencil; who is here to draw a picture of Mr Allen for the Exeter Hospital',[2] no drawing has as yet been identified. Allen, for many years one of Bath's leading citizens, had probably befriended Hoare from the beginning, and given him the entrée to his circle of particular friends, many of them literary men such as Fielding, Richardson and Pope. The portrait is a very straightforward one, and corresponds to Samuel

Cat 14

Derrick's description of Allen as 'a very grave well-looking old man, plain in his dress, resembling that of a quaker, and courteous in his behaviour'.[3] The only concession to grand portraiture, albeit a very underplayed one, is the swathe of curtain material in the background. The fact that the portrait was never engraved may also be due to the modesty of the sitter, for such an engraving would have been popular.

1. P.M.G. Russell, *A history of the Exeter Hospital*, 1976, pp 43–4.
2. Richard Hurd ed., *Letters from an eminent prelate*, 1809, p 267.
3. Samuel Derrick, *Letters*, 2 vols., 1767, Letter XXXIII 10 May 1763.

14a Ralph Allen

Medium: Black chalk heightened with white on buff paper, lightly squared 14⅜ × 11⅝ in 36.5 × 29.5 cm
Prov: Colonel Harold Malet, sold 1894 to British Museum
Coll: The Trustees of the British Museum

This drawing is one of a group made as records of finished works. In the case of those drawings which correspond to finished portraits, the copies are totally faithful. Although most of them are faintly squared, perhaps for ease of reduction, none were ever engraved. It is worth noting that there is a tradition, quoted by R. Wright, that Mary Hoare copied her father's paintings in little, but although the group of drawings to which this one belongs on the whole present a softer image of the sitters than do the paintings, they are too accomplished for someone in her teens.

Cat 14a

14b Ralph Allen
by Prince I Hoare

Medium: Marble bust 60 cm high
Prov: 1757, presented to the Royal Mineral Water Hospital by Dr Warburton

According to the Hospital Minutes for April 27 1757,

the Governors begged leave 'to return their thanks to the Revd Dr Warburton for his kind intention of making a present of a bust of Ralph Allen Esqr to the Hospital'. The sculptor, like the painter, has caught the natural gravity of the sitter, and by discarding the wig and draping the bust has underlined the antique virtues which Warburton recognized.[1]

1. An etched profile of Allen by William Hoare was used as frontispiece to editions of Warburton's *Moral and Political Dialogues* together with an inscription from Seneca which ends 'Nemo illum amabilem, qui non simul venerabilem diceret.'

15 Robert Dingley 1708–1781

Medium: Oil on canvas 50 × 40 in   126.9 × 101.6 cm
Prov: 1762, presented by William Hoare to the Magdalen Charity; Magdalen Trust sale, Christie's 21 March 1975 (130); Anon sale, Bonham's 25 Nov 1976 (109)
Coll: John Thompson Esq

Cat 14b

The inscription in Italian, *a un amico benemerenti*, strengthens the supposition that Dingley and Hoare met in Italy; Joseph Spence describes the sitter while in Rome in 1733 as 'pretty Mr Dingley . . . in love with one or two ladies at least by the earnestness with which he desires his humble service to them'.[1] A wealthy Russia merchant, Dingley became a noted philantropist and collaborated with another such, Jonas Hanway, particularly in the founding of the Magdalen Charity for repentant prostitutes. The inmates were not only sheltered from further vice but also trained to gainful employment. The Magdalen – like the Foundling Hospital before it – became a fashionable venue and Horace Walpole has left an entertaining description of a visit there. Dingley is painted in his capacity as Governor, seated at a table laden with documents and holding open on his knees a copy of *An account of the rise, progress and present state of the Magdalen Charity*, published in 1761 and opened to show the frontispiece: an illustration of a typical inmate.[2]

1. Joseph Spence, *Letters from the Grand Tour*, 1975, p 283.
2. W. S Lewis, *op.cit.*, vol 9, pp 273–4: Letter to Montagu 28 Jan 1760: '. . . and at the west were enclosed the sisterhood above an hundred and thirty, all in greyish brown stuffs, broad handkerchiefs, and flat straw hats with a blue ribband, pulled quite over their faces'.

Cat 15

15a Robert Dingley

Medium: Oil sketch on canvas 8 × 6½ in   20.3 × 16.5 cm
Coll: Private Collection

It is interesting to note that the sketch differs from the finished painting in one major respect. There is a swirl of lighter paint in the background which can be read as a kneeling figure, perhaps with a skull in the foreground. It is known that Dingley owned a painting of a Repentant Magdalen, and that another such picture was bequeathed to the Charity at a later date by another benefactor. It was probably felt that so popish a representation of repentance was not suitable for a protestant Charity and the juxtaposition of benefactor and semi-nude penitent not advisable for the boardroom.

Cat 15a

15b Robert Dingley

Medium: Mezzotint by Dixon, inscribed: *Robert Dingley Esqre Treasurer of the Magdalen House done from an original picture presented to that Charity by Mr William Hoare*
Lit: Chaloner Smith, *op.cit.*, vol I, p 209 (CS14)
Coll: National Portrait Gallery

Cat 15b

16 John Pitt of Encombe, Dorset, his Wife and Son (Plate 4)

Medium: Oil on canvas 55 × 46½ in   139.7. × 118 cm

Prov: Wm Morton Pitt (1754–1836); by family descent; Anon sale, Christies 2 May 1986 (lot 191); Anon sale, Sothebys 16 Nov 1988 (lot 62)

Exh: Society of Artists 1761 (42: A gentleman, his lady and child). In an annotated copy of the exhibition catalogue, Horace Walpole noted the names *John Pitt and Family*

Coll: Private Collection

William Hoare had joined the Society of Artists from its inception in 1760, but did not send any work to the first exhibition. We do not know whether he visited this exhibition, but if he did his attention was probably taken by Reynolds' full length of the Duchess of Hamilton against a landscape background, the portrait pastels of Cotes and Vispré's pastels with classical titles. Although this exhibition was only opened for two weeks in the Spring, upwards of 6,000 catalogues were sold. Such an opportunity to show his work to a greatly enlarged public would have prompted Hoare to choose a painting the following year which would stand up to competition and which he considered a representative specimen of his work to date.[1] He chose a group portrait of which there were quite a few during those years of maximum output but most of which are now untraced. The three members of the family are united in bonds of quiet affection highlighted by the placing of the hands. The colour scheme though lively is not garish and the sitters are shown against a parkland setting and stormy sky. Because of the decision to show both parents in a standing position while keeping to the ¾ length format, he had some difficulty in placing the child naturally and has had recourse to a grassy bank. This awkwardness reappears in some other paintings at this date (cat 20).

1. In 1761, Gainsborough exhibited his first full length (Mr Nugent) and Reynolds five portraits among which a powerful likeness of Lawrence Sterne and an equestrian portrait of Lord Ligonier.

16a John Pitt and Family

Medium: Oil on canvas 7½ × 6¾ in   19.2 ×
            17.3 cm
Prov: Anon sale, Sothebys 10 July 1980 (24)
Coll: Jacob Simon

A compositional sketch,[1] it set the pose and the
colour scheme for the patron's approval. That some
discussion followed can be seen from the fact that the
landscape details were changed around in the finished
painting. The more masculine temple was chosen as
background for John Pitt, who had a certain
reputation as an amateur architect,[2] whereas his wife
now stands against a gentler background of foliage and
sky.

1. Several of these sketches have appeared in the
    salerooms, some attributed to Francis Hayman, all are
    broadly painted with flat brushstrokes indicating form.
2. Encombe House which John Pitt inherited from his
    mother in 1734 now has added to its facade a
    pedimented doric loggia which (according to Pevsner)
    had originally been a garden feature.

Cat 16a

16b John Pitt and Family

Medium: Black chalk and stump on grey paper
            heightened with white
Prov: Colonel Harold J Malet, sold 1894 to
            British Museum
Coll: The Trustees of the British Museum

This is, like cat 14a, a faithful record of the finished
painting.

Cat 16b

17 Dr Oliver and Mr Peirce Examining Patients

Medium: Oil on canvas 42 × 69 in   1.25 × 1.69 m
Prov: Presented by the artist to the Hospital 1762
Exh: Society of Artists 1762 (38)
Coll: The Royal National Hospital for Rheumatic Diseases

Cat 17

This was always meant as a propaganda picture, and exhibited as such.[1] Horace Walpole was not enthusiastic, a note in his catalogue reads: 'Middling. Drs Oliver and Peirce examining patients', yet it was warmly reviewed in the press. The St James' Chronicle printed in May 22/23: 'One of the best pictures in the room – finely imagined, and admirably executed – all the figures are excellent: the Steward, the Surgeon, the sickly looks of each patient; and yet the different appearance of sickliness in the man, the woman, and the child; the scurf, and blotches on their hands; and every minute circumstance in the picture down to the velvet coat and the table, show great power of execution, and the most accurate observation of nature'. In his twenty years as Hospital Visitor, Hoare would have had ample opportunity to study disease at close quarters and it is more than probable that he was able to use inmates of the hospital as models.

The rectangular format of the painting, originally a Venetian invention, had been used in England since Van Dyck. The composition, however is interesting in another sense for it is quite closely based on one of the great Post-Reformation images: the *Supper at Emmaus* by Caravaggio (fig 2). An unlikely model for a Protestant institution, the early baroque drama has been softened down, the patients quietly await their turn, the lighting is rational and the brooding darkness hovering over St Peter is replaced by an explanatory engraving of the Hospital facade but strong similarities remain: the rising diagonal of heads from right to left, the head of Dr Oliver in sharp profile, the highly significant group of hands in the same off-centre position, the repoussoir figure at the bottom left hand corner. The Caravaggio painting is documented in the Villa Borghese in Rome from 1650 to 1787 and Hoare would have had many opportunities of seeing it as the collections were open to artists and visitors alike.

Fig 2

1.   The painting is listed in the 1761 Society of Artists exhibition catalogue as *A picture intended to be given to the Mineral Water Hospital.*

37

17a Royal Mineral Water Hospital Committee Book

Coll: The Royal National Hospital for
Rheumatic Diseases

On July 28th 1762,[1] at the weekly meeting at the
Royal Mineral Water Hospital which Prince I Hoare
attended, it was 'Ordered that the thanks of the
General Court be sent to Mr William Hoare for the
elegant Picture he has presented to this Hospital'. The
Hospital is fortunate in having retained all its early
Minute books which are an invaluable source of
information on the status of Hoare within the
community. Beginning as plain Mr Hoare in 1742,
the twenty-ninth member of the Court of Assistants,
he became a Governor in May 1779, 'by virtue of [his]
donations', and was henceforward entitled to the
appelation of Esq.

1. Committee Book V, p 119.

Cat 18

18 Lady Emily Kerr as a Bacchante

Medium: Oil on canvas 69½ × 57½ in 176.5 ×
146 cm
Prov: Painted for the sitter's father; Major R.C.
& Miss V Bridgeman, presented 1936 to
Holburne of Menstrie Museum
Exh: Edinburgh, National Portrait Gallery of
Scotland, *Van Dyck in check trousers*, 1978
(64)
Coll: The Trustees of the Holburne Museum and
Crafts Study Centre, Bath

Lady Whilelmina Frances (Emily) Kerr, daughter of
the 4th Marquess of Lothian, married at seventeen
Captain (later Lt-Gen Sir) John McLeod. When in
Bath as a very young girl she was praised for her
graceful dancing, and Hoare has chosen to depict her
as a bacchante in a deliberate attempt at a grand
historical portrait. In 1766, at the Society of Artists'
Exhibition, Reynolds had shown a portrait of *Mrs
Hale as Euphrosyne* (fig 3), where a full length female
figure in approximately classical dress is silhouetted
against the sky, with dancing figures crowding behind
her and in the lower distance. Mary Ann Hale was an
actress and it may seem odd that a similar composition
was thought suitable for Lady Emily. It must be said
that Hoare's rendering is very much more decorous,

Fig 3

not only are the background figures dancing round a statue of Flora,[1] not as unbridled as in the Reynolds and closer to classical prototypes as used by Poussin and Claude but the sitter's dress is altogether more demure, and the classically correct details throw a respectable antiquarian gloss over the whole.

1. The Farnese Flora and Hercules had long stood in the courtyard of the Farnese Palace in Rome, and Rysbrack had included copies of both within the Pantheon at Stourhead between 1759 and 1762. It is interesting to note that one of Gainsborough's few direct allusions to antiquity is the small model, probably by Cheere (2), of the Flora statue included in the portrait of his two daughters sketching, now in America.
2. Terracotta models of the Flora were available in the 18th century and one signed Cheere is at Stourhead. (cf J. Kenworthy-Browne, Rysbrack, Hercules and Pietro da Cortona, *Burlington Magazine*, 1983, vol 125, pp. 216–9).

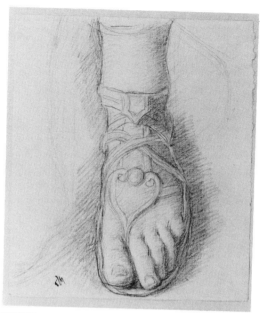

18a Studies of Sandalled Feet

Medium: Black chalk 7⅜ × 5⅛ in   18.7 × 13.3 cm 7½ × 5½ in 18.5 × 14 cm
Prov: Florence Ashton 1889; Album, Anon sale, Sotheby's 14 March 1985 (5)
Coll: Private Collection

The studies were probably made after antique sculpture. Hoare retained his interest in classical remains all his life, and was foremost in recording the new finds in Bath when the remains of the Roman Thermae came to light in 1752, making a sketch plan of the whole.[1]

1. The plan is now in the Manuscript Department of the British Museum.

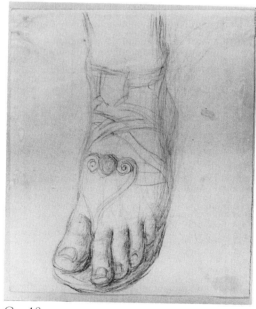

Cat 18a

19 The Three Sons of the 9th Earl of Lincoln
(Plate 5)

Medium: Oil on canvas 83 × 71 in   211 × 180.3
            cm
Prov: painted for the Earl of Lincoln; by family
            descent
Lit: *Clumber House catalogue* 1872, cat 66
Coll: The Trustees of the late 7th Duke of
            Newcastle

The three surviving sons[1] of the 9th Earl of Lincoln
(later 2nd Duke of Newcastle) are grouped against a
parkland landscape with a distant view of a lake and
bridge.[2] The Claudian overtones are strong and the
arcadian atmosphere reinforced by the stone plinth on
which the eldest boy is leaning, but any hint of
melancholy[3] is dispelled by the lively bright scarlet of
the boys' breeches and waistcoats. If one assumes that
the eldest boy is in his early teens, a date in the early
to mid 1760s seems likely.

1. Henry, Lord Clinton (1750–1778) who predeceased his
    father, the Hon Thomas Pelham-Clinton (1752–1795),
    later 3rd Duke, and the Hon John Pelham-Clinton
    (1755–1781).
2. The Clumber House catalogue suggests this is a view of
    Clumber Park, but the bridge built in 1763 was only of
    three arches (the lake was not recontoured until 1774),
    and Lord Lincoln's seat before 1768 was at Oatlands.
3. Their mother had died very suddenly in 1761.

20 Alicia Maria Carpenter, Countess of Egremont
?–1794

Medium: Oil on canvas 49 × 40 in   124.5 × 101.5
            cm
Prov: Painted for the 2nd Earl in 1762; by
            descent
Lit: *Catalogue of pictures at Petworth,* 1856
            (371); C.H. Collins Baker, *Catalogue of the
            Petworth collection of pictures in the
            possession of Lord Leconfield* 1920
Coll: The National Trust, Petworth House

Charles Wyndham, the future 2nd Earl of Egremont,
had made the Grand Tour from 1728 to 1730 partly
in the company of George Lyttelton and Henry
Bathurst, all were later to be patrons of William
Hoare, whom they most likely met in Italy. Lady

Cat 20

Egremont, noted for her beauty and the sweetness of her disposition, had been celebrated in verse by her husband's friend Lyttelton and in 1761 was appointed Lady of the Bedchamber to the new Queen Charlotte. Her hand resting on a grassy bank she is silhouetted against a dreamy parkland and sunset sky and is dressed in a creamy white dress and pale lavender stole, with long sleeves tied with matching bows. She always wore a pearl necklace round her neck to hide a small mole.

20a   Receipted Bill

Prov: Petworth Archives
Coll: Lord Egremont

The recto itemises the pictures painted by Hoare for the 2nd Earl of Egremont:

A half length of his Lordship   *31–10*
Do of Lady Egremont   *31–10*
A Full length of two children   *42 –*
Four Fancy Pictures in Frames 31–10

The verso is a receipt for the monies:

Sepr 28 1763 Recd the full Contents on the other side of the Right Honble the Countess of Egremont Extr of the late Earl of Egremont for the use of Mr William Hoare. Isaac Gosset.

The verso is further endorsed:

Hoare's Bill/for Portraits/ £136.10.0/paid 27 September 1763/ Hoare's bill £136.10.0

In a letter dated from Bath September 25 1763,[1] Hoare explains to Lady Egremont's man of affairs that he is sending his frame maker Isaac Gosset to collect the monies owed him. Lady Egremont, whose husband had died suddenly 'from an apoplexy which from his figure and the plethora he lived in was reasonably to be expected'[2] was settling all the outstanding bills as executrix to her husband and guardian to her son, the 3rd Earl.

1. Petworth Archives.
2. Lord Chesterfield in a letter to his son written from Blackheath, 22nd August 1763.

21 The Egremont Children 1762

Medium:	Black chalk and stump on grey paper heightened with white and lightly squared 17¼ × 13¾ in
Prov:	Colonel Harold J. Malet sold 1894 to British Museum
Coll:	The Trustees of the British Museum

A simple and natural portrait of two children, the pyramidal composition allowing the two heads to lean towards one another without strain. Lady Elizabeth Wyndham helps support her brother's sketchbook and gazes straight out of the canvas, her brother, the future 3rd Earl and patron of Turner, draws from a subject situated to his left. A few childhood drawings survive in the Petworth Archives and it is very likely that Hoare, who had taught two of his children as well as some of the younger members of the Stourhead family, gave the young boy some advice and encouragement. In 1764, the painting, now at Petworth, was hanging in the Countess's new dressing room in Petworth House, Piccadilly.

Cat 21

22 Henry Hoare the Magnificent 1705–1785 (Plate 6)

Medium:	Pastel 23 × 17 in 58.5 × 43.2 cm
Prov:	By family descent
Coll:	The Trustees of the Savernake Estate

This is a particularly fine pastel, probably the basis for several oil paintings of the sitter. Quite often, in Hoare's oeuvre, a pastel portrait of great psychological insight was the starting point for a more formal oil, as the medium particularly lent itself to capturing a fleeting and evanescent expression, the life-giving quality which Hoare must have admired in French pastellists such as La Tour and Perronneau. In almost pure profile, the portrait has a commanding quality and patrician presence which helps to explain the nickname Henry II was given within the family. It is a portrait drawn from the standpoint of mutual friendship and respect as can be gauged from those letters that remain.

23 Susannah Hoare, Lady Dungarvan (later Lady Ailesbury) 1732–1783 (Plate 7)

Medium: Pastel 23 × 17 in   58.5 × 43.2 cm
Prov: Framed at the same time as cat 18; by family descent.
Coll: The Trustees of the Savernake Estate

Susannah, one of Henry II's two daughters from his second marriage, was first married (1753) to Lord Dungarvan, son and heir to the Earl of Cork & Orrery, a close neighbour of her father's. The marriage, uniting wealth with title, may not have been a particularly happy one, and friction between the two fathers is apparent from those letters which are still extant. Dungarvan died early in 1757 and for the intervening years until her second marriage to Lord Bruce (later Earl of Ailesbury) Susannah lived at Stourhead with her father. She is dressed in becoming half mourning, the pink silk of her gown enhanced by delicate black ruching. A widow's cap crowns her powdered hair and she is employed in a form of netting or tatting. It was becoming fashionable for ladies to be depicted employed in 'domestic' pursuits.

24 A/L From William Hoare to Henry Hoare

Coll: Hoare of Stourhead records deposited in Wiltshire County Record Office (383/907)

Dated Bath June 5 1760, this long letter ranges from thanks for the congratulations sent on his daughter's winning a premium at the Society of Arts, and his ideas on her training, to a discussion of some of Ovid's verses sent by Henry describing Ariadne's rescue by Bacchus and Carracci's treatment of the subject 'I think tho Carracche never wants Greatness, nor Emotion, yet there is generally too great a heaviness in his Figures, un poco troppo del Grasso di Bologna'. William goes on to disagree with Webb's[1] strictures on Guido Reni whom he particularly admired: 'there is a singular delicacy in Guido equal or above the usual ideas in the Antique'. He continues detailing his appreciation of the Old Masters: 'The Transfiguration [Raphael's] I hold miraculous . . . the whole idea is as high as human power can conceive' He places Domenichino 'next to Raphael' and prefers him to Guido because 'he always leaves something to exercise and lead on as it were the imagination'. Unlike Webb, Hoare does not have too high an opinion of antique painting, believing it useless to discuss works which are no longer in existence. What does remain, 'Ornaments of the Emperors' Palaces and Grottos . . . have a great sameness . . . Figures all in a row, not like the modern intermixtures and dispositions, nor with any attempt of Perspective or backgrounds'. In this respect Raphael is 'much superior for he has so perforated his Picture as to open a space incredible, where the Antients would have had nothing at all'. Correggio has 'his admiration and indulgence'[2] but he thought Leonardo had 'been exalted beyond his merits', his works 'are not without an attempt at Grace and Roundness but there is too much of black and discordancy in his shade'. He ends with a discussion on the best wallpaper against which to hang pictures, sends his congratulations to Susannah Hoare, Lady Dungarvan, on her engagement to Lord Bruce (later Earl of Ailesbury) and invites himself to Stourhead for a few days 'when you should be most disengaged that I might enjoy your Virtù within and without'. A postcript announces the sending of a gift (see cat 33)

1. Daniel Webb (1719–98), an Irishman educated at Oxford, later resided chiefly in Bath. In 1760 he had just published *An Inquiry into the beauties of painting*.
2. Mariette had expressed the same sentiment (see Biographical sketch, note 17).

Cat 25

25　**Captain Philip Thicknesse** 1719–1792
26　**Anne Ford, Mrs Thicknesse** 1737–1824

Medium:　Black and red chalk heightened with white
　　　　　14¼ × 11¾　in 36.8 × 29.8 cm
Prov:　　Col Harold Malet sold 1894 to British Museum
Coll:　　The Trustees of the British Museum

These two drawings are records of paintings the present whereabouts of which are unknown and which may have been marriage portraits. Gainsborough had already painted Anne Ford[1] but the companion picture was never carried out and this led to a rift betwen artist and sitter. Thicknesse must have been pleased with the result of the commission to Hoare, for even as late as 1778 he wrote in his New Prose Bath Guide: 'It is almost needless to mention Mr Hoare, whose long residence at Bath has made his genius for painting in crayons and in oil universally known; and when genius and moral character are

Cat 26

united in the same man, he becomes doubly respectable; & in this predicament Mr Hoare has stood in our memory upwards of 30 years'.

1. *The Autobiography and Correspondence of Mary Granville, Mrs Delaney*, 1861 vol III, p 605. The Gainsborough portrait was 'a most extraordinary figure, handsome and bold; but I should be sorry to have anyone I loved painted in such a manner'

27 Uvedale Tomkins Price of Foxley 1685–1764

Medium:	Oil on canvas $4^{3}/_{10} \times 3^{7}/_{10}$ in 10.6 × 9 cm
Coll:	Jacob Simon

This sketch relates very closely to a painting advertised by Shepherd's Gallery before the war as by Robert Edge Pine. The painting is now untraced but both the oil sketch and the drawing (see cat 27a) are so typical of others by Hoare that the attribution of the painting to Pine cannot hold.

Cat 27

27a Uvedale Tomkins Price of Foxley

Medium:	Black chalk on buff paper, heightened with white $10^{5}/_{8} \times 10$ in 27 × 25.5 cm
Prov:	Col Harold J. Malet, sold 1874 to the British Museum
Coll:	The Trustees of the British Museum

This more detailed record of the painting makes an interesting comparison with the portrait of the same sitter by Gainsborough now in the Alte Pinakothek, Munich. The two portraits are both dateable to the very early 1760s and it would be interesting to know whether they were commissioned simultaneously in friendly rivalry or otherwise. Both artists have presented Price as the personification of the connoisseur and amateur artist. Gainsborough shows him as a collector of landscape drawings, Hoare as an amateur of antique sculpture, and in both cases, the presence of a porte-crayon suggests that Price was

Cat 27a

capable of drawing. In the Hoare portrait, a small cast of *Minerva* stands on a shelf and a drawing from an antique head is propped against a pile of books. The head is that of the *Venus with a shell* from the Borghese Gallery, seen from below as she would have been by any young student crouching on a low stool.[1]

1. A cast of this popular statue (Scheemakers, among others, had brought one back from Italy) is shown on a high plinth in Wright of Derby's *Academy by Lamplight* of 1769 which illustrates the conditions under which students learned to draw from the antique.

Cat 28

28–31 The Four Seasons

Medium: Pastels 23 × 17⅜ in   58.5 × 43.5 cm
Prov: Westhorpe Hall, Notts sale, Christies 19 Nov 1985 (195)
Coll: Mr and Mrs Nigel Cayzer

Some of Rosalba's most popular subjects were the *Four Seasons*, where four partly clothed young women showed off their charms with perfect propriety under the guise of allegory. The vogue for them was such that Dingley even wrote to Rosalba herself trying to jump the queue and appropriate a set promised to Consul Smith in Venice. Rosalba's figures were purely decorative, but Hoare's are a distillation of memories of antique sculpture. Several sets of four are documented, and there must be more, one in the Coffee Room at Wilton,[1] one in the collection of Dr Charlton, physician to both the Hoare and Gainsborough families,[2] perhaps the *Four fancy Pictures* included in Lady Ailesbury's bill,[3] and Lady Egremont's (cat 20a). A '*Spring*' and '*Summer*' were bequeathed to Sir Richard Colt Hoare by Prince II Hoare as *Herculaneum Nymphs*, a title perhaps given to them after the resumption of interest in the excavations in that city. As the four were repeated

Cat 29

46

over many years, the style changes from a soft rococo to a harder-edged neoclassicism, to which the set exhibited here in the main belongs.

The four designs are all variations on the theme of antique Venuses. *Spring*'s hairstyle, with the short top curls and the loose tresses escaping from a chignon is found in, among others, the Crouching Venus (Uffizzi) and the Capitoline Venus. *Summer*'s pose is adapted from the Venus Callypiga in the Farnese Collection. *Autumn*'s hairstyle with a fillet can also be seen in many antique statues and *Winter*, though fully clothed, holds the pose of the Medici Venus.[4]

1. *Aedes Pembrochianae* 1788 11th ed., 'The four seasons in crayons by Mr Hoare'
2. An anonymous sale catalogue advertised in the Bath Chronicle for Thursday 27 November 1794 mentions 'particularly the FOUR SEASONS by Hoare purchased out of the collection of the late Dr Charlton'
3. The bill, including frames, came to £63.00.
4. In her pastel portrait at Coughton Court, Lady Throckmorton chose to be represented in the same pose and costume as Winter.

Cat 30

Cat 31

32 The Pool of Bethesda

Medium: Oil on canvas. It has not been possible to include this picture in the exhibition on account of its great size.

Prov: painted for the Octagon Chapel; signed and dated 1765

Coll: Bath Masonic Hall Association

Cat 32

Built by Lightholer as a proprietary chapel, the Octagon was opened to the public with a performance of Handel's Messiah on 4 October 1767. Though luxurious in its appointments, it did not meet with universal acclaim, 'a handsome building, but not like a place of worship, there being fireplaces in it, especially on each side of the altar, which I cannot think at all decent'.[1]

The decoration of churches was still a question for debate, and commissions for altarpieces infrequent, but it is very probable that, on commissioning the altarpiece the Trustees had in mind St Mary Redcliffe in Bristol for which church Hogarth had painted a very large triptych[2] some ten years previously. Hoare chose to illustrate a passage in the New Testament,[3] picking the moment when the angel has charged the water with healing powers and is returning heavenwards; the theme could not have been better suited to a spa town. Healing the sick was one of the Seven Acts of Mercy but it had never been a popular subject on the Continent. Caravaggio had painted all seven Acts in one canvas and Domenichino had included a *Healing* in the ceiling of S Andrea della Valle in Rome. More recently, Hogarth had used the subject for his decoration of the staircase of St Bartholomew's Hospital in London in 1736, a swirling composition in a rococo frame. Hoare's own design lacks tension, what should have been the emotional centre of the composition, the angel rising in a glory while the sick bathe in the healing water, lacks conviction, and the foreground figures seem to be acting out their role against a backcloth.

1. *The diary of a country parson, the Rev James Woodforde 1758–81*, 5 vols 1924–31, entry for January 23 1769.
2. An Ascension, flanked by a Sealing of the Tomb and The Three Maries at the Sepuchre.
3. John V 2–8: *A pool . . . called . . . Bethesda, having five porches. In these lay a great multitude of impotent folk, of blind, halt, withered, waiting for the moving of the water.*

33 A Sleeping Nymph

Medium:	Pastel 23¾ × 32 in 60.3 × 81.3 cm
Prov:	1760, presented to Henry Hoare by William Hoare
Coll:	The National Trust, Stourhead

William Hoare wrote to Henry II on June 5th 1760 from Bath: 'As I know you have a favourite sleeping nymph in your garden, I have made another in a dress something different, which I must beg your acceptance of just as a memorial that I am very much in your debt. I wait for its frame from London.'[1] William Hoare has conflated several prototypes instantly recognizable to anyone who had studied classical sculpture in situ, so that the pastel could almost be read as a sculptural *cappriccio*; the cold colour scheme, where the figure is starkly silhouetted against a deep sapphire background, and the blue shadows in the drapery folds enhances this sculptural impression. The sleeping figure is that of the Sleeping Ariadne,[2] one of the sights of Rome, a painted lead copy of which was even then resting at the centre of the Stourhead grotto. The folds of the background hanging, originally an antique form, had remained in favour throughout medieval and renaissance times, forming the bottom tier of many fresco schemes. The buttoned mattress however had a much more interesting history. Lorenzo Bernini had been asked to sculpt such a mattress by Cardinal Borghese in 1620 as a base for the statue of the *Sleeping Hermaphrodite* in his collection. Bernini's technical brilliance was such that the mattress became almost more famous than the statue. Both William and Henry Hoare would have been familiar with the Borghese collection, but the original memory was probably rekindled by Delvaux, Hoare's companion in Rome, who had sculpted other reclining figures on similar mattresses for the Earl of Bedford.[3]

1. Wiltshire County Record Office, Hoare of Stourhead papers 383/907.
2. Penny and Haskell, *Taste and the Antique*, 1981, pp 184–7. During most of the XVIIIth century, the statue was known as a Sleeping Cleopatra.
3. Charles Avery, Delvaux and the Duke of Bedford, *Apollo* 1983, p 312–321.

34 Susannah Hoare, Countess of Ailesbury
1732–1783

Cat 34

Medium: Oil on canvas oval 50 × 40 in   127 × 101.5 cm
Prov: By descent
Coll: The Trustees of the Savernake Estate

This may be the portrait begun by Arthur Pond and radically altered for the better by William Hoare as is described in a letter from Henry II to his son-in-law Lord Bruce, later Earl of Ailesbury: 'Stourhead April 7 1765, I hope dear Lady Bruce looks as well as . . . her picture here which Mr Hoare has this morning altered in the dress and shape amazingly for the better, new earrings, a pearl necklace, a better hat and feather, an improved neck and shape and tip of the ear, and lengthened ruff makes a sweet figure altogether such as Sir Peter Paul Rubens would have hung over enamoured with looks of cordial love'.[1] Lord Cork, Lady Bruce's first father-in-law had thought highly of Pond, recommending him to his wife[2] but the quality of the original likeness may be gauged from the head and shoulders by Pond now at Stourhead. As several drawings and copies show,[3] Hoare was a great admirer of Rubens and familiar with his work both at home and abroad, and his adaptation of Rubens's portrait of his second wife goes far beyond the surface details of a costume which in an earlier decade had been a stock in trade of masquerade dress, and there has been a real effort at immitating Rubens's flesh tones.

1. Wiltshire County Record Office, Hoare of Stourhead papers S 27
2. Lady Cork and Orrery, *Orrery Papers* 1903, p 164: letter of 14th April 1741: 'Pond will be best for your picture'.
3. In 1762, Henry Hoare paid William the very large sum of £200 for a full scale copy in pastel of the painting in the Pembroke collection, now called Jordaens but then ascribed to Rubens. *Mr Hoare of Bath for 4 boys after Rubens £200.00.* (Henry Hoare's Private Account book 1739–1770, Hoare's Bank).

35 **The Hon Edward Clive** (later 2nd Baron Clive
     & 1st Earl of Powis) 1754–1839

Medium: Pastel 30 × 25 in   76.2 × 63.5 cm
Prov: Presented as a leaving portrait to Eton
            College
Coll: The Provost and Fellows of Eton College

Cat 35

Edward Clive was at Eton from 1762 to 1770, and the
pastel must date from the latter year. Although called
Hoare by Cust,[1] it has also in the past been attributed
to Lawrence, quite improbably, as the latter was only
born in 1769, but typically of the reluctance to
acknowledge Hoare as a skilled portraitist. It belongs
to that period of Hoare's development, when already
an elderly man, he is very responsive to the grace and
lightness of Gainsborough's late Bath period.
Although the colour scheme is of the simplest, the
surface is not dull as he has been able to convey the
fall of light on to the cloth of the coat, and the
immaturity of the sitter's features with great subtlety.

1.   L. Cust, *Eton leaving portraits*, 1910, cat 14.

36 John Quicke of Newton St Cyres 1724–1776
37 Jane Coster, Mrs John Quicke

Medium: Pastel 59.4 × 44.3 cm
Prov: By family descent
Coll: Private Collection

John Quicke married in 1759, as her second husband,
Jane Hoblyn, the daughter of Thomas Coster of
Bristol from whom she inherited a considerable
fortune. John Quicke seems to have made the Grand
Tour and collected casts of antique statues, and as
remaining letters suggest, was a close friend of Lord
Dungarvan.[1] The very restrained palette of these two
pastels is reminiscent of Greuze's scenes of domestic
genre, implying a life of virtuous simplicity.

1.   Devon Record Office, Quicke Archives.

Cat 36

38   Masters Thomas and John Quicke (Plate 8)

Medium: Pastel 62.0 × 74.7 cm
Prov: By family descent
Exh: Perhaps Royal Academy 1770 (cat 104 –
             Portraits of two children in crayons)
Coll: Private Collection

Genre scenes of children playing games had already
been seen in England in the work of Philip Mercier,
but the influence here is even more directly French
and comes from Chardin, some of whose work was
known in England both in the original and through
engravings. Hoare seems to have attempted to capture
Chardin's calm stillness in the elder boy's pose but
decided to break it by the younger boy's eager
insistence on continuing the puzzle. In 1763, John
Spilsbury, engraver and map maker, described himself
in a tradesman's Directory as 'a Map-dissector in
wood, in order to facilitate the teaching of
Geography'. The first map so dissected was one of
England, but in about 1766 he was offering, at a cost
of twelve shillings, 'Europe dissected into its kingdoms
mounted on mahogany [3mm thick] and backed with
white paper to stop buckling, the countries coloured

Cat 37

in outline'. As late as 1809, Richard and Elizabeth Edgeworth in their *Essays on Practical Education* were recommending that maps should be dissected by boundaries of sea and land. There is no attempt at interlocking as in modern puzzles and the younger boy is holding 'Italy' in his hands and looking to his brother for confirmation that he is placing it in the correct position.

1. Linda Hannas, *The English jigsaw puzzle 1760–1890*, 1972.

39   Christopher Anstey and His Daughter Mary

Medium: Oil on canvas 49⅝ × 39¼ in   126 × 99 cm
Prov: Mrs C.M. Sambourne-Palmer bequeathed 1940 to National Portrait Gallery
Exh: Royal Academy 1779 (cat 130 – A gentleman and his daughter half lengths)
Coll: The National Portrait Gallery

Cat 39

Christopher Anstey only removed permanently to Bath in 1770, some years after his great success with *The New Bath Guide* in 1766,[1] taking up residence at 4 The Crescent. The informality and immediacy of the sitter's pose, half rising to greet the incomer, the spontaneity of the little girl's gesture trying to retain her father's attention, make this a sympathetic study of family life. From the middle of the century, children were no longer expected to look and behave as miniature adults and family relationships were allowed to exist on a less formal footing. If this new sensibility had its theoretical beginnings in France in such writings as Rousseau's, early English conversation-pieces which included children had already captured some of this feeling though usually in a more robust way; as the century progressed, more and more children's portraits were commissioned and the new sensitivity became prevalent. The little girl's doll is dressed in the latest fashion with a very high headdress.

1. W S Lewis, *op. cit.*, vol 10, p 218. Letter to George Montagu 20 June 1766: 'There is a new thing published that will make you bepiss your cheeks with laughing . . . . .it is called the New Bath Guide . . . . .I can say it by heart'

40 Daniel Danvers ?–1780

Medium: Oil on canvas 50 × 40 in 127 ×
101.5 cm
Inscribed, signed and dated: *Danl. Danvers
Esqr/late Treasurer of this House/from 1760
to 1779/Wm Hoare pinx./1780*
Prov: 1780 presented to the Hospital by William
Hoare
Exh: Bath, Victoria Art Gallery, *Ralph Allen and
his circle,* 1964 (cat 17)
Bath, Holburne of Menstrie Museum,
Hospital Exhibition, 1988
Coll: The Royal National Hospital for
Rheumatic Diseases

Cat 40

A partner in a Bristol Bank (Cam, Whitehead,
Danvers and Philloy),[1] Danvers had looked after the
Bath Hospital accounts from 1760. The Hospital
Minutes for 13 December 1780 record the gift: 'The
thanks of the Board were given to William Hoare Esq.
for his valuable present to this Hospital of the picture
of the late Daniel Danvers Esq'. This intimate portrait
of a man seated at his work shares many of the
qualities of cat 39,[2] the same soft feathery brush
strokes which show the lasting influence of
Gainsborough and the same ability to capture the
fleeting moment, and to convey arrested motion and
interrupted speech.

1. Dr Macnamara, *Memorials of the Danvers Family,*
   privately printed 1895.
2. These qualities are also found a very few years
   previously in Nathaniel Dance's *Arthur Murphy* of 1777.

41 Mrs Elizabeth Hoare ?–1794

Medium: Black and red chalk 6½ × 8⅛ in 16.5
× 20.6 cm
Prov: Florence Ashton; Album, Anon sale
Sotheby's 14 March 1985 (5)
Coll: Private Collection

Typical of the profile portraits Hoare made of his
family and intimates this drawing probably dates from
the late 1740s. Mrs Hoare is elegantly dressed in a
black lace fichu, a cap held down by a goffered frill,
and a triple row pearl neck-lace.

Cat 41

42   Anne Hoare 1751–1821

Medium: Black and red chalk 10⅛ × 7⅞ in   25.8
             × 20.2 cm
Prov: Sir Robert Witt
Coll: Courtauld Galleries (Witt Coll 3574)

Anne Hoare, William's second daughter, is shown as
a demure little girl, quiet and neat. This is an
unusually finished, and posed, drawing among the very
many William Hoare made of his family.

Cat 42

43   Dr William Borlase 1695–1772

Medium: Black and red chalk 7½ × 5¾ in
Prov: The sitter; St Asaph Family; W.C.
             Borlase, by descent.
Coll: Mrs P. Mallet

The drawing is signed and inscribed *Hoare Bath/8ber
1757/Aetatis 62*. In a letter dated 27 October 1757,
Borlase wrote 'I presented Mr Hoare with no 411
[presumably one of his own publications] as he
presented me with my picture in crayon'. A friend and
relation of Dr Oliver, Dr Borlase had been persuaded
to try the waters at Bath from 1730. A member of the
Ralph Allen circle, he furnished Pope with many
mineral samples for the Twickenham grotto, and had
pretensions to connoisseurship, counselling van Diest,
then patronised by Allen, to 'lay aside the dull,
insipid face painting [and] go into battle as van der
Meulen did'".[1] A noted antiquary, he helped Nash
with the design of the Obelisk set up in Queen Sqare
in honour of the Prince of Wales' visit in 1734.

1. W.C. Borlase, *The Descent, name and arms of Borlase of
Borlase in the County of Cornwall*, 1888 p 182.
This letter is dated October 8 1739.

Cat 43

44   The New Bath Guide

Coll: Trustess of Gainsborough's House Society,
             Sudbury, Suffolk (Gift of Cavendish
             Morton Esq)

This copy of a volume of satirical verse, which was
published by Anstey in 1766 and ran to many
editions, was the property of a Miss Dorothy

Richardson who visited Bath in 1770.[1] She used the blank sheets at the back of the book to jot down some of her impressions. Miss Richardson and her party visited the studios of both Gainsborough and Hoare on the same day, a pattern which seems to repeat itself in other diaries.[2] She mentions 18 works by Hoare, among which are: *A child holding a porte-crayon* (Prince II – Victoria & Albert Museum), *Miss Hoare leaning upon a drawing book* (Mary – Private Collection), *A girl reading* (probably Anne – Private Collection). Artists often put aside separate rooms in their house where they could hang their works so that the influx of visitors, though gratifying, should not interrupt their work and intrude upon sittings. Their servants showed the public around, and a gratuity was expected.

1. Hugh Belsey, A visit to the studios of Gainsborough and Hoare, *Burlington Magazine*, 1987, vol 129, pp 107–9.
2. Elizabeth Noel saw "nothing capital in either", though she was rather struck, at Hoare's, by a portrait of the notorious Duchess of Kingston 'in her weeds and looking at a picture of the Duke'. (M.Elwin, *The Noels and the Millbankes: their letters 1767–92*, 1967, pp 37–8).

45   Sketches after Venus, Flora, Cupid & Mars by Paris Bordone

Medium: Red and black chalk 3½ × 5¾ in 8.9 × 14.6 cm
Prov: Florence Ashton; Album, Anon sale Sotheby's, 14 March 1985 (5)
Coll: Private Collection

These two studies made in Italy[1] illustrate Hoare's wide ranging interest in the Venetian school. He has drawn a rapid and lively composition sketch to act as an aide-memoire for the whole composition but more interestingly has drawn a separate and more detailed study of the entwined arms and hands, showing an early interest in the use of hands to express feeling, an interest he was to develop in later paintings. Both drawings are examples of 'the many designs' brought back by Hoare from Italy as mentioned by Vertue.

1. The Bordone, now in the Hermitage, Leningrad, only arrived in Russia between 1774 and 1783.

Cat 45

46 **Sketch after The Nurture Of Jupiter by Castiglione**

47 **Sketch after Rinaldo and Armida by Van Dyck**

Medium: Coloured chalks 7½ × 8⅝ in 18.5 × 22 cm
7½ × 8½ in 18.5 × 21 cm

Prov: Florence Ashton 1889; Album, Anon sale Sotheby's 14 March 1985 (5)

Coll: Private Collection

Hoare maintained his interest in the Old Masters throughout his life and these two sketches were made when he was staying with Lord Lincoln,[1] probably at the time he was painting Pelham family portraits in London. Both sketches, though only roughly blocked in, follow the original design closely and show how much Hoare was still interested in the type of grand design he had so little chance of attempting.

1. The Nurture of Jupiter is inscribed in pencil on the verso: *Lincoln/Exchequer*. The sketches presumably date between Lord Lincoln's appointment as Auditor in 1751 and his becoming 2nd Duke of Newcastle in 1768.

Cat 46

Cat 47

48 Children Playing in a Park

Medium: Black and red chalks 10 × 7½ in   25.5 × 18.5 cm
Prov: Florence Ashton 1889; Album, Anon sale, Sotheby's 15 March 1985 (5)
Coll: Private Collection

It is very possible that this drawing was made at Stourhead, where Henry Hoare liked being host to an extended family, William's only grandson among them. A tender, spontaneous drawing of small children at play, the nervous line indicates how swiftly the drawing was made and gives vivacity to the whole.

Cat 48

49 Study for a St Cecilia

Medium: Red chalk 13⅜ × 8½ in 34 × 18.5 cm
Coll: Private Collection

This drawing seems, like many other compositional ideas in the late years, to be a personal reaction to subjects painted by others, and never to be taken any further. In 1775, Reynolds had exhibited at the Royal Academy a portrait of *Mrs Sheridan as St Cecilia* (fig 4).[1] This picture had attracted a lot of notice in the press and had been praised for its antique simplicity. Hoare's saint, with her upturned gaze and rapt expression is a close relation to the Saints and Sybils of Guido Reni and Domenichino, for whom Hoare had always felt great admiration (cf cat 24) and whom Reynolds had also admired.

1. The painting is now in the Los Angeles County Museum of Art (William Randolph Hearst Collection).

Cat 49

Fig 4

50 Head of a Girl

Medium: Red and black chalks 11¾ × 7⅞ in 28.8
          × 20 cm
Coll: Victoria Art Gallery, Bath City Council

This very late drawing defines form solely through
light and shade, the highlights of the face floating to
the surface from a background of fine hatched lines.

Cat 50

51 Ruins in a Landscape
    by William Hoare Jnr

Medium: Pencil and watercolour 9⅛ × 7⅛
          in   24.3 × 17.9 cm
Coll: Leeds City Art Gallery

The watercolour, with its strong overtones of the
Norwich School, is obviously the work of an amateur,
the signature matches that on the letter mentioned in
the introduction (The Hoare Family, note 2) and
those on many pencil sketches of landscapes, mostly
Welsh.

Cat 51

52 Sketchbook belonging to Mary Hoare

Prov: Probably part of Prince II Hoare's bequest to the Royal Academy

Coll: The Royal Academy of Arts

The sketchbook, with its front marbled cover inscribed *Mary Hoare/ Bath . . .* in ink, was at some later date used as a scrapbook in which small engravings were pasted. In some cases the engravings have fallen off and the sketchbook is opened at such a page showing an early drawing where the awkwardly rendered shadows flatten the lower half of the figure and the perspective of the chair is misunderstood. In the early 1760s, Mary's father had painted Mrs Thicknesse, seated and playing the lute (cat 26).

Cat 52

53 R.H.A. Bennet Esq. of Beckenham, Kent
?–1814

Medium: Black and red chalks 8 × 5½ in 21.4 × 13.7 cm

Prov: Mrs Tritton sale, Christies 18 Nov 1983 (115) as William Hoare

Coll: Private Collection

Mr Bennet, a neighbour of Henry and Mary Hoare at Beckenham, was the husband of one of the daughters of Sir Peter Burrell. She and her two sisters, later Countess of Beverley and Duchess of Hamilton, were particular friends of Mary. The drawing is inscribed on the verso: *By Mrs Hoare of Beckenham/R.H.A. Bennet Esq./ of Beckenham in Kent & Northcourt – Isle of Wight/ died March 1814.* The inscription was incorrectly transcribed onto the backing board the *Mrs* being rendered as *Wm.* The style of drawing is quite unlike anything by William and very close to other drawings known to be by Mary, and her authorship cannot really be in doubt.

Cat 53

54 **Self Portrait** by Prince Hoare

Medium: Oil on canvas 63.5 × 52.7 cm
Prov: 1834 bequeathed by Prince to Joseph Bonomi;1880 bequeathed by the latter to the Royal Academy
Exh: 1868 South Kensington, National Portraits (835)
1883 Royal Academy, Winter Exhibition (223 – as by P Hoare and T Gainsborough)
Coll: Royal Academy of Arts

Self portraits have always necessitated the use of mirrors but this fact is generally concealed. In this instance Prince II seems to enjoy the spatial ambiguity. We are left in doubt as to whether we are seeing a section of wall on which hangs a framed portrait in profile or, since we do not see the subject full or even three-quarter face, are we looking at a mirror and seeing a profile reflected from another mirror, a complex visual game, allowing the artist to set down his own profile. The features are those of a very young man and may have been painted before Prince II's departure for Italy in 1776 when he was twenty one as it is less self confident than the self portraits painted for the Grand Duke of Tuscany's Gallery at the Uffizzi a very few years later.

Cat 54

55 **William Hoare, RA** by Prince Hoare

Medium: Oil on canvas 30 × 25 in
Prov: Probably one of the 'family portraits' bequeathed as heirlooms to Sir Richard Colt Hoare by Prince II Hoare in 1834
Coll: The National Trust, Stourhead

In October 1794, Joseph Farington saw this portrait in the studio of S.W. Reynolds, the engraver, who was proposing a series of engraved portraits of Royal Academicians, and had borrowed various portraits to copy. Farington remonstrated that a similar scheme was already well on the way, Bestland the engraver having commissioned Henry Singleton for a group portrait (*The Royal Academicians in 1793*) which he was even then engraving. Farington also remarks in his diary that he thought S.W. Reynolds 'unqualified as an artist for such an undertaking'.[1] In the event, Reynolds's scheme came to nothing, and only a very few portraits were engraved, William Hoare's among them (cat 55a).

1. *The Diaries of Joseph Farington*, Yale ed, I/251–2.

Cat 55

55a **William Hoare, R.A.**

Medium: Mezzotint by S.W. Reynolds
Coll: Victoria Art Gallery, Bath City Council

The plate was printed originally in 1794 and again in 1796 with an added address. A much reduced version (2⅛ × 1¾ in) appeared at the head of a memoir on Hoare in *Essex, Suffolk and Norfolk Characters* published in 1820.

Cat 55a